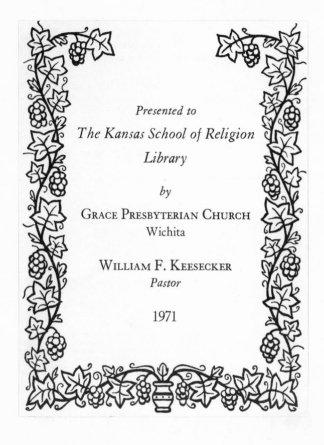

Presented to

The Kansas School of Religion
Library

by

GRACE PRESBYTERIAN CHURCH
Wichita

WILLIAM F. KEESECKER
Pastor

1971

Science & Secularity

THE ETHICS OF TECHNOLOGY

IAN G. BARBOUR

Science & Secularity

THE ETHICS OF TECHNOLOGY

1817

HARPER & ROW, PUBLISHERS

NEW YORK, EVANSTON, AND LONDON

technology - philosophy
ethics

FIRST EDITION

LIBRARY OF CONGRESS CATALOG CARD NUMBER: 77-109886

TO JOHN, BLAIR, FREE, AND HEATHER
*who have helped me to see
some of the things wrong with the present
and some of the potentialities of the future—
which will be theirs*

CONTENTS

Introduction

In the nineteenth century the main challenge to religion came from evolution. But the church has now abandoned the biblical literalism which conflicted with Darwin's theory of evolution. Today the challenges come mainly from the general characteristics of science itself. The first three chapters of this volume examine three of these challenges: *the scientific method, the autonomy of nature,* and *the technological mentality.* These reflect three aspects of science: science as a way of knowing, science as a way of looking at nature, and science as a way of controlling the world. If pure science is a form of knowledge, applied science is a form of power, and both have profoundly influenced attitudes toward religion.

But there are also new challenges arising from particular fields of scientific discovery. As forms of knowledge, these discoveries have important intellectual implications; as forms of power, they raise significant ethical issues. In Chapter Four, recent work in *molecular biology* (DNA) is considered, both in its implications for our view of man, and in relation to the ethics of genetic control. Chapter Five deals with *cybernetics,* first by comparing computers and brains, and then by noting ethical problems in automation and systems analysis. The final chapter takes up some urgent problems of *science policy,* particularly the crises of population and pollution, as well as the wider question of the redirection of technology to serve human welfare.

The first three chapters, which look at challenges arising from the general characteristics of science, seek also to identify the facets of secularity which have been encouraged by contemporary science, and to relate them to contemporary religion. We will see that *secularity* is a complex set of attitudes of which some are congenial to the biblical outlook and some inimical. *Secularism,* on the other hand, is an alternative naturalistic faith which is incompatible with biblical faith. The chief components of secularity are the following cluster of related ideas: First, interests are *this-worldly* rather than otherworldly. Attention is directed to life here and now. Second, *the autonomy of secular knowledge* is assumed. The world can be understood by man's independent reason. Third, there is *confidence in man's creative capacities,* especially his ability to order his own life and control his own destiny. Fourth, all institutions operate in *autonomy from ecclesiastical control.* Daily life is carried out in independence of institutional religion; there is a separation of church not only from state, but from educational, economic, and social activities. Specialized institutions are organized around limited objectives.

A fifth facet of secularity is *skepticism about inclusive world views.* There is doubt, not just about Christian metaphysics—which once provided an overarching system and a fixed frame of reference—but about the very possibility of a single, unified world view. There is suspicion of total explanations, comprehensive systems, and ethical absolutes as such. Instead, pragmatic answers are sought for particular problems. Limited goals are pursued and provisional solutions are accepted. There is a greater tentativeness, tolerance, recognition of pluralism, and willingness to live with partial insights. No human institution or claim of knowledge can be absolutized. It is this fifth component of secularity which is violated by secularism when it becomes a new ideology making absolute claims as an all-encompassing world view.

We will be interested in those aspects of secularity which

reflect *the influence of science.* The scientist seeks knowledge of nature without any reference to God. He views it as an autonomous order in which natural forces follow their own laws of cause and effect. Nature can be understood and utilized; it is at man's disposal, available for his conquest. In applied science and technology it is man who controls nature; the effective power is human rather than divine. Through his own abilities man reached the moon. Secular man trusts science, not God, to fulfill his needs. He expects to alter human genes, travel to Mars, and create "electronic brains" which rival human intelligence. He declares his intellectual autonomy through the scientific method and his practical autonomy through the technological control of his own destiny. These are the scientific components of secularity with which contemporary religion must come to terms.

Since each chapter closes with a summary, it would be superfluous to summarize them here. However, it may be helpful to indicate some of the distinctive themes which run throughout the volume, starting from science as knowledge and moving toward science as power. The first four themes are somewhat philosophical; the next three are more theological, and the final three practical and ethical. Yet they are all closely interrelated. Each has a bearing on the challenge of science to religion today.

1. Cognitive Models. A prominent feature of the methods of contemporary science is the role of models. Theoretical models are partial and inadequate ways of imagining what is not observable. They are symbolic representations, for particular purposes, of aspects of reality which are not directly accessible to us. A conceptual model of the electron, for example, is not a literal picture of reality; but neither is it, at the opposite extreme, simply a useful fiction or a convenient calculating device. Sometimes two or more models of the same entity may be used under differing conditions. We will examine several kinds of model, ranging from the "billiard-ball model" of a gas to computer models of political, economic, military, and transportation systems. We will see also that recent writings in the philosophy of science have stressed the role of the knower and the importance of creative imagination. Science, it appears, is not quite so objective—nor religion so subjective—as the empiricists have claimed. Secularity rightly insists that science is autonomous and its methods are distinctive, but they are not totally unlike those of other fields of inquiry. Science does not displace all other approaches to experience, for diverse types of model serve diverse functions in human life.

2. *Models of Man.* The breakthrough in molecular biology (particularly the breaking of the genetic code of DNA, the "secret of life"), and the great advances in the "artificial intelligence" of computers, have reinforced the conviction of some interpreters that "man is just a machine." Against such reductionism, I will argue that the models of man as a biochemical organism and as a responsible self are not mutually exclusive. Let us acknowledge man's unity with nature and his biological basis (for which impressive evidence will be cited from molecular biology, neurophysiology, evolutionary theory and ecology). But let us also recognize that organisms are multileveled systems; events at higher levels of organization, especially in man, are without parallel at lower levels. Man, in short, can be viewed both as a biochemical mechanism and as a responsible self.

3. *Interdependence.* There is a new ecological awareness of the interconnectedness of all forms of life and of man's dependence on his environment. Man's pollution of water and air, exploitation of natural resources, and heedless use of pesticides and detergents have ravaged nature and now threaten human life. Another example of interdependence is the new field of systems analysis which treats complex systems as integrated wholes. Again, cybernetics is the control of total systems through the feedback of information about their behavior. In an interdependent society, technological innovations have far-reaching effects; we can no longer let the development of applied science depend largely on corporation profits. The planning of technological change must be a central issue in national policy, as we will see below. The individualistic values of the past will have to give place to the social values of an interconnected world in which we breathe or suffocate, thrive or perish, together.

4. The Open Future. Various forms of determinism are rejected in this volume. Against scientific determinism (the predictability of classical physics), I set forth the indeterminism of quantum physics and evolutionary biology. Against technological determinism (the idea that technology is an inevitable and uncontrollable force), I suggest that man can direct technology, though he has failed to do so in the past. Against theological determinism (the classical concept of an omnipotent God), an alternative model of God is presented (see following paragraph). There is, at every moment, a variety of possible futures. Man invents the future, choosing among open possibilities. Today we have an unprecedented experience of change, a capacity to imagine new alternatives, a power to alter the future. Evolution is not a complete process; it continues into the future. Like the ideas of "models" and "interdependence," the concept of "possibility" is a motif which recurs repeatedly in these chapters.

These are also three themes which are more theological in character:

1. Divine Persuasion. The openness of the future is inconsistent with predestination and predetermination. Belief in the autonomy of nature and the freedom of man, which are legitimate facets of secularity, call into question the classical concept of divine omnipotence. In place of the traditional model of a God of coercion (the potter and the clay), or the Deistic model (the clockmaker and the clock), process theology has developed the model of a God of persuasion (the father and the growing child). God's power is the power of love, which evokes man's response but does not compel. Both man and nature have their own integrity, which God respects. Process thought has emphasized the themes of open possibilities and interdependence; it has expressed a dynamic and evolutionary view of the world. Moreover, it provides a theology of nature (something sadly lacking in both existentialism, which retreats to the realm of man's inwardness, and neo-orthodoxy, which sees nature as the stage for the drama of man's redemption). I will suggest that the absence of an adequate theology of nature is one of the roots of our ecological crisis.

2. *Human Responsibility.* Man has acquired greatly increased powers over himself and his environment. He can alter his genes, influence the future course of evolution, and transform or destroy his world. An important aspect of secularity is insistence on human responsibility, and here the contemporary theologian can concur. God is not predominantly the represser of human vitalities, the authoritarian ruler who keeps man submissive and dependent; he is the fulfiller of man, evoking our creative capacities. We are called to be co-creators in an unfinished universe, participants in God's ongoing purposes. We can indeed defend man's maturity and responsibility, "man come of age." But I maintain that we do not have to share secular man's unlimited confidence in his own abilities. Here the biblical tradition is more realistic in pointing to man's ambivalence, his rationalization of self-interest, his alienation from his fellow man. Modern man seeks autonomy from external authority, but he may remain in bondage to internal forces; the transforming power of love sets man free for a life of service and involvement in the world.

3. *Christian Secularity.* We are called, then, to the affirmation of life in the world, to celebration of the secular, to involvement rather than otherworldly renunciation. Only a false dichotomy places "secular" over against "sacred." Secular existence is precisely the sphere of our religious responsibility. The gospel is not the enemy of human freedom and maturity; it liberates us to become more fully human. We can concur also with secularity in insisting on the autonomy of political and educational institutions from ecclesiastical control. There is a new vision of the servant church as a community of joint search and engagement in the world, a prophetic witness to social justice, racial equality, and a more humane society. The gospel liberates us from bondage to the past, for no social order is absolute or sacrosanct. We are free to reshape all institutions. The biblical concern for personal existence and interpersonal relationships has new significance in the face of the depersonalizing and dehumanizing impact of a technological society. Note that all three of these theological themes—"divine persuasion," "human responsibility," and "Christian secularity"—

represent the recovery of genuinely biblical ideas which were somewhat neglected in classical Christendom (with its defense of divine omnipotence, otherworldliness, and ecclesiastical hegemony).

Finally, there are three ethical questions which arise repeatedly:

1. The Technological Mentality. Modern man's attitude of mastery and control does have considerable biblical support. The psalmist acknowledges man's unique status: "Thou hast given him dominion over the works of thy hands; thou hast put all things under his feet." But without the concomitant biblical ideas of care and respect for nature, dominion has turned into arrogance and ruthless subjugation. Today it is not enough to seek piecemeal technical solutions for each successive symptom of environmental deterioration; unless basic attitudes are changed, man's predatory spirit will only find new ways to plunder the earth. In place of an image of man over against nature we must foster recognition of the interdependence of the community of life. In place of exploitation we must cultivate reverence for life and respect for the integrity of the natural order. We need an ecological conscience, an environmental ethic, growing out of a theology of nature. Moreover, preoccupation with technology leads to the impoverishment of man's experience, the dehumanization of existence, the loss of the imaginative life expressed in poetry and art. The calculating attitude of mastery excludes the openness and receptivity which interpersonal relationships require. Some of our youth have been aware of these dangers, and have asserted the priority of personal over impersonal life, spontaneity over control. Unqualified devotion to technology can become a Promethean quest for omnipotence, a confidence in science as the source of salvation. Secularity has then turned into secularism, and man's distinctively human existence is in jeopardy. This is perhaps the crucial motif of the book, since it is technology rather than pure science which now has the major impact on our life and our thought. A crisis of values lies behind the visible crises of our technological society.

2. The Ethics of Novelty. We now face ethical choices which have never arisen before in human history. For the first time, the population explosion threatens to produce famine, overcrowding, and environmental catastrophe. Yet if population growth can be controlled, automation promises a high level of productivity and a great increase of leisure. This would call for a quite different ethic of leisure from anything which was appropriate in the past. Never before have choices concerning genetic alteration or cybernetic systems been confronted. In such unprecedented situations, with options which never existed previously, advice from traditions formulated under different conditions is not likely to be helpful. We must be prepared to embark with courage and imagination on new paths if they will contribute to human fulfillment. But openness to the new does not imply that just because a technological development is possible it must inevitably occur. The prophetic ethic of responsibility for the future demands careful analysis of the social and individual consequences of each of these specific options.

3. The Redirection of Technology. A number of questions of science policy are considered in these chapters. The most urgent are the control of nuclear weapons and the limitation of population growth. The next decade will be crucial for the future of mankind. War and pollution, the murderous offspring of our technology, are in danger of destroying our society; these crises require the mobilization of our efforts and resources before it is too late. I will argue also that technical assistance to underdeveloped countries and the rehabilitation of urban ghettos—that is, attention to hunger and poverty on our own globe—should have higher priority than landing a man on Mars. The social planning of technology is required, not just to prevent harmful consequences, but to promote socially desirable changes. Such momentous decisions cannot be left to the vagaries of the market place, but must be directed through political institutions. Decision-making power need not be centralized in a technical elite; basic policy questions can be subject to democratic control. Here the challenge to religion is ethical rather than philosophical or theological. It is, basically, the question of whether science will serve man, or the reverse.

A final word of acknowledgment is in order. Earlier versions of the first four chapters were the James A. Gray Lectures presented at Duke University. Portions of several chapters were given as the Earl Lectures at the Pacific School of Religion in Berkeley. In preparing the manuscript for publication I have added footnotes and expanded a number of paragraphs, but otherwise have not altered the somewhat informal style of the original lectures.

CHAPTER ONE

The Scientific Method

ATLANTA, GA., Nov. 9—God, creator of the universe, ultimate reality of Christians, and most eminent of all divinities, died late yesterday during major surgery.

In an exclusive interview this morning, Dr. Thomas Altizer, Dr. Paul van Buren, and Dr. William Hamilton, surgeons in the unsuccessful operation, stated: "The death was not unexpected; he had been ailing for some time and lived much longer than most of us thought possible."

Reaction from the world's great and from the man on the street was uniformly incredulous.

Former president Harry S. Truman, who received the news in his barbershop in Independence, Mo. said: "I'm always sorry to hear somebody is dead. It's a damn shame."

A housewife in an Elmira, N.Y. supermarket commented: "I never met him, but from what I heard I guess he was a real nice fellow. At least he's out of his misery."[1]

That notice appeared in *Motive* magazine shortly after three young theologians proclaimed that God is dead. Was the obituary premature—or was it a case of mistaken identity?

The first challenge to religion today is the widely held conviction that the scientific method is the only reliable path to truth. Science seems to yield indubitable knowledge on which all men can agree. Its objectivity seems to contrast with the subjectivity of religion. Here we will be concerned with *science as a way of knowing*. We will be analyzing the intellectual autonomy of modern man, secularity in the realm of thought. The discussion will be more philosophical and the issues more abstract than those of subsequent chapters. But the challenge is a fundamental one, for if the credibility of religious beliefs is undermined, other aspects of religious life cannot long survive.

In the popular stereotype, the scientific method consists of precise observation followed by logical reasoning. The stereotype leaves out the role of *creative imagination* in the formulation of scientific theories. A theory is never given to us ready-made in the data; it is a human invention, a mental construct.[2] The role of the knowing subject and the character of creative imagination can be brought out by focusing attention on the use of models in science, which I will then compare with the use of models in religion. Subsequent chapters will deal with specific models of God, of man, and of society.

I. Models in Science

There are in science a number of different kinds of model which serve a diversity of functions. They are used, that is, for very diverse purposes. First, there are *experimental models* which can actually be constructed. These include replicas or "scale models" representing spatial relationships, and "working models" representing temporal sequences. Think of a wind-tunnel model of an airplane, from which the lifting force of a particular wing design can be measured. In an "analogue model," certain features of one system are simulated by the behavior of another system in a different medium—for example, a hydraulic flow model of an economic system, or an electrical circuit model of an acoustic system. Such models are used to solve practical problems when it is difficult to experiment on the primary system, or when the relevant mathematical equations are unknown or too complex to solve. In these cases one physical system is actually built to serve as a model of another physical system.[3]

Second, at the opposite extreme, there are *logical models.* The logician or the pure mathematician starts from the axioms and theorems of a formal deductive system. A logical model is a particular set of entities which satisfy these axioms and theorems. For example, a set of points and lines in geometry is a logical model for Euclid's formal axioms. The mathematician uses it to illustrate the abstract system and to give a possible interpretation of it. Note that here he is dealing entirely in the realm of ideas; neither the formal system nor the model of it is a physical system.[4]

Third, *mathematical models* are between these two extremes. They are symbolic representations of selected aspects of physical or social systems. Examples might be the equations expressing the relations between the pressure and volume of a gas, supply and demand in economics, or the growth of a population in time. Now a mathematical model may in turn be physically represented by the electrical circuits of a computer. In Chapter Five I will be discussing computer models of economic, political, military, and transportation systems. At the moment, the point to note is that a mathematical model resembles the primary system only in formal structure; there are no material or physical similarities. It is a symbolic representation of particular features of a physical system, and its chief use is to predict the behavior of the latter.

My main concern, however, is a fourth kind: *theoretical models.* These are imaginative mental constructs invented to account for observed phenomena. This kind of model is usually an imagined mechanism or process, which is postulated by analogy with familiar mechanisms or processes. I will suggest that its chief use is to help one understand the world, not simply to make predictions. But I will also suggest that it is not a literal picture of the world. Like a mathematical model, it is a symbolic representation of a physical system, but it differs in its intent to represent the underlying structure of the world. It is used to develop a theory which in some sense explains the phenomena. And its origination seems to require a special kind of creative imagination.

As an example, consider *the billiard-ball model* of a gas. Start with a box full of a gas, such as air, and imagine that the gas is composed of very tiny elastic spheres bouncing around. If we now imagine that the mechanical behavior of the hypothetical spheres is similar to the behavior of colliding billiard balls, we can develop a theory. The theory involves equations interrelating the mass, velocity, energy, and momentum, attributed to the tiny spheres or particles. Of course, none of these theoretical properties can be observed. But the model also suggests that some of the theoretical properties attributed to the invisible particles might be correlated with observable properties of the gas (for example, the momentum change of the particles colliding with the containing wall might be identified with the pressure of the gas). With these assumptions we can derive several of the experimental Gas Laws which you may dimly recall from high school physics—Boyle's Law, for instance, which states that when you reduce the volume of a gas by 50 per cent, then the pressure of the gas will double. The model thus leads to a theory, and the theory accounts for patterns in experimental observations.

Three features of the billiard-ball model, and others like it, should be noted:

1. Models are analogical. Similarities with a familiar situation are posited in some respects, and differences are posited in other respects. Thus our hypothetical tiny elastic spheres were assumed to have mass and velocity, as billiard balls do, but not color. Notice that the analogies postulated may be physical (e.g., elasticity and mass), and not simply formal as in the case of logical or mathematical models. In the origination of a novel theory the scientist may propose a model incorporating positive analogies drawn from several familiar situations, together with radically new assumptions introduced by a further act of creative imagination. There is implicit or explicit reference to what is familiar and previously intelligible, but there is also considerable novelty and freedom in imagining a model. One can assign to it whatever properties one thinks might contribute fruitfully to the theory.

The history of science provides many examples of this combination of *analogy* and *innovation* in the creation of models which were useful in generating theories. The "Bohr model" of the atom, in which "planetary" electrons revolve in orbits around a central nucleus, resembled the solar system in certain of its properties; but the key assumption of quantum jumps between orbits had no classical parallel at all. Among more recent examples is the "liquid drop model" of the nucleus of the atom. In each case the model aided the formulation of the equations of the theory and also suggested plausible correlations between certain theoretical terms and observable variables.

2. *Models contribute to the extension of theories.* The use of a model may encourage the application of a theory to new kinds of phenomena. Through the use of the billiard-ball model, the equations of the theory of gases were applied to new experimental domains (including gas diffusion, viscosity, and heat conduction) which involved types of observation very different from those of the gas laws. A model may also be instrumental in the modification of the theory itself. It was the model, not the formalism of the theory, which suggested that one might go on to postulate particles having a finite size and attracting each other; when the theory was thus amended, van der Waals' Equation for gases under high pressure could be derived. The revised model—elastic spheres with attractive forces—departs from the simple billiard-ball model, yet it would never have occurred to anyone without the latter. Mary Hesse has argued persuasively that because of their suggestiveness and open-endedness models and the analogies they embody are a continuing source of plausible hypotheses.[5]

3. *A model is intelligible as a unit.* It provides a mental picture whose unity can be more readily understood than that of a set of abstract equations. A model is grasped as a whole; it gives in vivid form a summary of complex relationships. Because of its immediacy and intelligibility it is frequently used for teaching purposes to help students understand a theory. But even at the critical stages of scientific discovery itself, scientists often report that visual imagery predominates over verbal or mathematical thinking.[6] Images are creative expressions of the

human imagination in the sciences as in the humanities. There are, of course, no rules for creativity, but analogies and models have frequently suggested new kinds of connection and new ways of looking at phenomena.

However, several words of caution are needed. The "intuitive intelligibility" of a model is no guarantee at all concerning its validity; deductions from the theory to which the model leads must be carefully *tested* against observations, and more often than not the proposed model must be amended or discarded. Models are not advanced as guaranteed truths; they are used to generate hypotheses to investigate. They are a source of promising theories to test. Again, a model need not be *picturable*, though it must be conceivable. Visualizable features may be selectively suppressed, as when we imagine colorless elastic spheres. Theoretical models, in sum, have three important characteristics: they are analogical, extensible, and unitary.

But now we must ask: What is the relation between a model and the real world? At the one extreme, models have sometimes been taken as *literal descriptions* of the world or as "pictures of reality." Lord Kelvin said in 1884: "I never satisfy myself until I can make a mechanical model of a thing."[7] But such literalism always runs the risk that one will push an analogy too far and neglect important differences between the new situation and the familiar analogue. Thus the analogy between light waves and sound waves, which was so fruitful at one stage in the history of science, led to the erroneous assumption that light, like sound, must be transmitted through a medium (the hypothetical "aether"). The nineteenth-century predilection for picturable mechanical models has been thoroughly undermined by quantum physics, which has shown that the atomic world is very unlike the world of familiar objects.

Partly in response to the inadequacies of literalism, postivistic scientists and philosophers went to the opposite extreme and thought of models as *useful fictions*. A model, they said, is neither true nor false; it is only more or less useful. They regarded models as temporary psychological aids in setting up theoretical equations; having served their purpose, they should be discarded. They are "disreputable understudies for mathematical formulas," or, in Duhem's words, "props for feeble minds." Even the more cautious empiricists, such as Richard Braithwaite, consider models to be dispensable; they are only "a convenient way of thinking about the structure of the theory."[8] He urges us to avoid all reference to such unobservable entities as elastic particles. I have been maintaining, on the contrary, that models have a continuing function. For it is often the model and not the theory which provides the clues for modifying the theory or applying it to new domains. Models have complex associations not present in the bare theoretical equation; the analogies are physical and substantive, not merely formal.

I would argue that we do not have to choose between literalism at the one extreme and fictionalism at the other. Let us grant that a model is a mental construct and not a picture of reality. It is a partial and selective attempt to represent symbolically, for particular purposes, aspects of a world whose structure is not accessible to us. No direct comparison of model and world is possible. But let us preserve the scientist's *realistic intent* in his use of theoretical models. He seeks to understand, and not simply to predict. The extension of theories seems to require that models and the questions they suggest be assigned a more important status than the ficitionalist view allows. It seems to me that the scientist today usually takes his models *seriously but not literally.* Models are partial and inadequate ways of imagining what is not observable. They remain hypothetical, reflecting an implicit "as if," a tentative commitment. The scientist believes that his postulated entities (e.g., gas particles) actually exist, but he does not hold that they are literally similar to the familiar objects (e.g., billiard balls) in terms of which he conceives of them.

The character of a scientist's *commitment to a model* may vary widely in the course of its history. When it is first introduced, it may be used very tentatively for very limited purposes, correlating a narrow range of phenomena. But the scientist tries to develop a consistent model covering as many aspects of the phenomena as possible. As its scope and reliability increase he has greater confidence in it. In the process, the model may be altered considerably; we saw that the model of gas particles came to include features such as mutual attraction which are not found at all in billiard balls. The model becomes more complex, and draws from many other analogies besides the initial one. (The original model can still be employed as a useful approximation, but it is then recognized as a deliberate simplification.) In our example, there have been further modifications under the impact of quantum physics; a great many analogies besides those with billiard balls have contributed to the most recent models of a gas particle.

I must add a word about the peculiar status of models in modern physics. *Particle* models, such as the billiard-ball model, dominated the classical physics of matter after Newton. By the nineteenth century another basic type of model, that of *waves* in continuous media, was also being employed for a different group of phenomena involving light and electromagnetism. In the quantum physics of the twentieth century, strange to say, both *particle* and *wave models* are employed for *all* entities in the domain of the very small—gas particles, electrons, photons of light, etc. Electrons, for instance, sometimes show spread-out interference patterns characteristic of waves, and at other times behave like localized discrete particles. Yet there is no way to combine wave and particle into one unified model. A unified mathematical formalism can be constructed to correlate observations statistically, but it does not yield predictions of individual observations.[9]

Now the positivist finds in this wave-particle paradox support for his conviction that we should *abandon all models.* He urges us to give up trying to imagine what goes on between observations. He wants us to look on the abstract equations as mere calculating devices for correlating observations. I would myself see the wave-particle paradox as a strong *warning against literalism* rather than as evidence for the rejection of models. Even the apparently bare equations of quantum theory carried imaginative associations. These may not have been pictorial in character but they conveyed analogies which were important in suggesting how the equations could be interpreted, extended to new domains, and modified. We still refer to "Schrödinger's wave equation"; Dirac's theory of "holes" still presupposes a particle analogy. We can't avoid using wave-like and particle-like terminology.

This is essentially Niels Bohr's conclusion—that we should retain *complementary models* but recognize their limitations. Bohr pointed out that the more a particular experimental arrangement makes wave-like behavior evident, the less evident is particle-like behavior, and vice versa. He also stressed the conceptual limitations of human understanding. We cannot know the world as it is in itself. If we try, as it were, to force nature into certain conceptual molds, we preclude the full use of other molds. We must choose between causal *or* spatio-temporal descriptions, between accurate knowledge of position *or* momentum, between adequate wave *or* particle models. We use successive and incomplete complementary models that cannot be neatly unified.[10]

Let me *summarize* the main points so far. First, models have a variety of uses in science. They serve diverse functions, some practical and some theoretical. Second, theoretical models are novel mental constructions. They originate in a combination of analogy to the familiar and creative imagination in inventing the new. Third, such models are taken seriously but not literally. They are neither pictures of reality nor useful fictions; they are partial and inadequate ways of imagining what is not observable. As Leonard Nash concludes:

We must not then take the theoretic model too literally: *indeed we may err by taking the model too literally.* But, as we would realize the full power inherent in it, *we must take the model very seriously.*[11]

II. Models in Religion

I want to turn now to the role of models in religion. One of their functions, as I see it, is to interpret certain distinctive kinds of experience. Among the basic experiences of religion are the following:

1. Awe and reverence. Men in many cultures have described a sense of the numinous, of mystery and wonder. Others have spoken of holiness and sacredness in a variety of contexts. Often there seems to be a sense of otherness, confrontation and encounter, or of being grasped and laid hold of. Correspondingly, man is aware of his own dependence, finitude, and contingency.

2. Moral obligation. Decision on ethical questions sometimes has an ultimate urgency, an inescapable responsibility which entails the subordination of one's own inclinations. Though the voice of conscience is in part the product of social conditioning, it apparently is not entirely so; it may lead a person to oppose his society even at the risk of death. Like each of these areas of experience, moral obligation is subject to a variety of interpretations.

3. Reorientation and reconciliation. In individual life, acknowledgment of guilt and repentance may be followed by the experience of forgiveness. Persons unable to accept themselves are somehow enabled to do so. Such reorientation may lead to a new joy and freedom from anxiety, an openness to new possibilities in one's life, a sensitivity to other persons. Grace is experienced between man and man; the healing power of love is at work in our midst when reconciliation overcomes estrangement.

4. Key historical events. In addition to individual aspects of religious experience, the data of religion include the corporate experience of communities which have arisen in response to historical events. Key events in the past continue to illuminate the present life of a community. In H. R. Niebuhr's words, "such events help us understand ourselves and what has happened to us."[12] The message of the Hebrew prophets was an interpretation of the pattern of events in Israel's national life. The Christian community arose in response to the life of Christ, which is the continuing center of its historical memory.

Now I want to suggest that there are *analogies* between these experiences and other events in man's life which suggest particular interpretive models. Edwyn Bevan has tried to show that a number of common religious symbols are based on such analogies.[13] He maintains, for example, that the sense of religious awe is similar to the awe men feel in looking up at a mountain or at the sky. Height is also associated with recognition of power, as when men kneel before the elevated throne of a king in acknowledging his authority over them. Symbols of *height* are therefore appropriate expressions of worship (e.g., "the high and lofty One"). Similarly, analogies with the experience of standing in a dazzling light may lie behind the frequency of *light* symbolism in religion. Bevan also discusses the use of such personal symbols as *spirit*. Perhaps the experience of reconciliation, in particular, may suggest analogies with interpersonal relationships. The sense of confrontation, otherness, and encounter, as well as the element of unexpectedness, seem to point to an activity independent of our control.[14] The character of our response thus leads us to postulate models of that to which we are responding.

Models are also used in the interpretation of the *corporate experience* of a community. Israel interpreted the pattern of events in her national life as the working out of a divine covenant analogous to the covenantal agreements familiar in the ancient world. Historical situations were interpreted by the prophets in relation to an image of God and his purposes for the nation. In the prophetic literature, various specific kinds of person are the analogues for models of God as King, Judge, Shepherd, Husband, Father, etc., and these images are used to understand corporate as well as individual experience. The Christian community came to take the person of Christ as a model of God—though for three centuries it debated what kind of "model" Christ was.

Thus models in religion, like scientific models, are analogical. They are also *extensible* and *unitary*. Images which originated in religious experience and historical events were extended to interpret other areas of individual and corporate experience. As models of an unobservable electron allow one to interpret new and unexpected patterns of experience in the laboratory, so models of an unobservable God allow one to interpret new patterns of experience in human life. Ultimate interpretive models—whether of a personal God or of an impersonal cosmic process—are organizing images which restructure one's perception of the world. One may notice features which might otherwise have been ignored. Moreover, religious models are readily grasped as unitary wholes. Because of their vividness and immediacy, they are strongly evocative of personal response.

The idea of *complementary models,* developed in modern physics, can perhaps also be applied in religion, as Bohr himself proposed. William Austin takes the images of God as Judge and as Father to be such complementary models used to interpret human experience.[15] One model, which stresses God's justice, prevents the exclusive development of the other which stresses love, and vice versa. In the prophetic literature one model or the other may be dominant in a particular historical situation, but each limits the use of the other. I will consider in the next chapter a number of alternative models of God; in Chapter Four, alternative models of man are discussed.

Next, I would submit that religious models, like scientific ones, should be taken seriously but not literally. On the one hand, they are *not literal pictures of reality.* In the biblical tradition the limitations of models are recognized. The prohibition of graven images "or any likeness" (Exod. 20:4) is both a rejection of idolatry and an acknowledgment that God cannot be adequately represented in visual imagery. "His ways are not our ways," for he is "beyond our farthest thought." Perhaps with auditory symbols (e.g., "The Word," "The Voice of the Lord") one is less tempted to think one can visualize God. Biblical language is reticent about claiming to describe God as he is in himself, though it uses models freely. The creative theologian, like the creative scientist, realizes that his models are not exhaustive descriptions. Neither God nor the electron can be pictured. Neither is at all like the objects of our familiar experience.

But if we insist that models are not literal descriptions, can we avoid the opposite extreme of treating them as *useful fictions?* Braithwaite, who considers scientific models dispensable, in turn treats religious language as a morally useful fiction.[16] Its function is to express and evoke distinctive ethical attitudes. Stories about God, he says, are parables whose only point is to recommend attitudes. We don't ask whether they are true or false, but how they are used. Parables are imaginative ways of endorsing an ethical policy or affirming one's commitment to a pattern of life. They are declarations of one's intention to act in a particular way—with unselfish love, for example. A model of God would then be a psychologically helpful fiction which supports moral behavior.

Now we must grant that religious models, like scientific ones, do indeed serve *a diversity of functions.* Contemporary philosophers have shown some of the varied ways in which religious language is used. Sometimes it does, as Braithwaite says, recommend a way of life or endorse a set of moral principles. Again, it may express and evoke a distinctive self-commitment. It may propose a particular kind of self-understanding or engender a characteristic set of attitudes toward human existence. It produces, that is, a typical form of personal life-orientation. Religious language may also express gratitude, dependence, and worship.[17] But beyond all these uses, I would insist that it also directs attention to particular patterns in events. It provides a perspective on the world and an interpretation of history and human experience. The religious believer, like the scientist, seeks to understand; his intent is realistic. His interests are theoretical as well as practical. He takes his models more seriously than fictionalism would allow. Here again we can avoid both literalism and fictionalism.

III.   Observation and Theory in Science

But we must now confront directly a major difference between models in science and in religion. Scientific models lead to *theories* which can be tested against objective experimental *data*. Surely religious models cannot be similarly tested. Let us turn back to science, then, to consider the process by which theories are tested.

There are a number of *criteria* by which scientific theories are assessed. *Simplicity* is sought both as a practical advantage and as an intellectual ideal. This includes not only simplicity of mathematical form and conceptual simplicity, but also an aesthetic element. It is not uncommon to hear scientists refer to the beauty or elegance or symmetry of a theory. Further, *coherence* with other theories is sought. The scientist aims at the comprehensive unification of separate laws, the systematic interrelation of theories, the portrayal of underlying similarities in apparently diverse phenomena. But the most important criterion is the number and variety of *supporting experimental evidence.* However, the relation between theory and observation turns out to be problematic.

There are *no bare uninterpreted data* in science. Expectations influence perceptions, both in everyday life and in science. Man supplies the categories of interpretation, right from the start. A doctor sees an X-ray plate differently from someone without medical training. Galileo saw a swinging pendulum as an object with inertia (which almost repeats its oscillating motion), whereas his predecessors had seen it as a constrained falling object (which slowly attains its final state of rest). The process of measurement, and the very language in which results are reported, are influenced by prior theories. The predicates we use in describing the world, and the categories with which we classify events, depend on the kinds of regularities we anticipate. The presuppositions which the scientist brings to his inquiry influence the way he formulates a problem, the kind of apparatus he builds, and the type of concept he considers promising. Theory, in short, permeates observation. As N. R. Hanson puts it, "all data are already theory-laden."[18]

I would want to insist, however, that there is a very wide variation in the degree to which any given *observation* is dependent on any given *theory.* In most experiments the data are relatively independent of the immediate hypothesis being tested; therefore the observations do exert some control over the hypothesis. Expectations do not completely determine what we see; unexpected events may make us revise our expectations. When two theories conflict, their protagonists can withdraw, not to a supposedly pure observation-language, but to an observation-language whose theoretical assumptions are not at issue. There will usually be enough overlap between the assumptions of the two parties that a common core of observation-statements can be accepted by both.

But note that the shared *observational core,* against which the competing theories may be tested, is not free of *conceptual interpretation.* The overlapping assumptions common to two theories will differ in different periods of history; they carry no guarantee of infallibility. Moreover, the categories of classification employed in an observational description may themselves need to be revised in the light of subsequent developments in the theory. This means that though observation exerts a control over theory, any given observation statement may find itself outvoted in the end and subject to modification.[19]

Thus the line between *observation* and *theory* is not sharp or fixed. The decision to look on a given statement as primarily theoretical or primarily observational is relative, pragmatic, and context-dependent. The emphasis may shift with the advance of science and the immediate purposes of inquiry. The "standard observables" of one period will differ from those of another. What you treat as basic and uninterpreted will also vary according to the theory you are testing. Those descriptions which you consider more stable and more directly accessible will be taken as data, but that judgment will itself reflect theoretical assumptions.

Most of the time, of course, scientists work within *a framework of thought* which they have inherited. As P. K. Feyerabend has pointed out, most scientists in their day-to-day work presuppose the concepts and broad background theories of their day. In testing theories of limited scope they can obtain unambiguous data which can be described in a commonly accepted observation-language. But when the background theory itself is at issue, when the fundamental assumptions and basic concepts are under attack, then the dependence of measurement on theoretical assumptions is crucial. For example, in the switch from classical physics to relativity, the meaning of all the terms

changed. "Time," "length," "mass," "velocity," even the notion of "simultaneity," all have different meanings in the new
framework.[20]

Thomas Kuhn, in his influential book, *The Structure of Scientific
Revolutions,* maintains that every branch of science is dominated
by a cluster of very broad conceptual and methodological presuppositions embodied in what he calls a *paradigm*—that is, a
"standard example" through which students learn the accepted
theories of the field. Because such an example also serves as a
norm of what constitutes good science, it transmits methodological and metaphysical assumptions as well as key concepts.
A paradigm (such as Newton's work in mechanics) implicitly
defines for a given scientific community the types of question
that may legitimately be asked, the types of explanation that are
to be sought, and the types of solution that are acceptable. It
molds the scientist's assumptions as to what kinds of entity
there are in the world and what methods of inquiry are suitable.

Kuhn shows how scientific communities *resist changes in paradigm.* Experimental evidence which is inconsistent with a prevailing paradigm is often set aside as an unexplained anomaly.
To take one example, Newton's theory of gravitation predicted
that the apogee of the moon's elliptical orbit around the earth
should move forward $1\frac{1}{2}°$ each revolution, but he admitted in
his *Principia* that the observed motion was twice that predicted.
For sixty years this disagreement, which was far beyond the
limits of experimental error, could not be accounted for, and
yet it did not overthrow the theory.[21] Sometimes special *ad hoc*
hypotheses are introduced to preserve a theory in the face of
discordant data. A complex theory of great generality, such as
the theory of evolution, is almost impossible to disprove merely
by citing incompatible evidence. Such a theory is abandoned
only when there is an alternative available. A theory which is
defective at a few points is better than none at all! In the absence
of an alternative, one can usually doctor up the old theory.

Kuhn says that when a major change of paradigm does occur
it has such far-reaching effects that it amounts to *a scientific
revolution.* A new paradigm replaces the old; it is not merely one
more addition to a cumulative structure of ideas. A revolution

(from Aristotelian to Newtonian physics, for instance, or from classical physics to relativity) is "a transformation of the scientific imagination" in which old data are seen in entirely new ways. For a brief period, adherents of two different paradigms may be competing for the allegiance of their colleagues, and the choice is not unequivocally determined by the normal criteria of research. Kuhn writes:

> Though each may hope to convert the other to his way of seeing his science and its problems, neither may hope to prove his case. The competition between paradigms is not the sort of battle that can be resolved by proofs. . . . Before they can hope to communicate fully, one group or the other must experience the conversion that we have been calling a paradigm shift. Just because it is a transition between incommensurables, the transition between competing paradigms cannot be made a step at a time, forced by logic and neutral experience. Like a gestalt switch it must occur all at once or not at all.[22]

Scientists resist such revolutions because previous commitments have permeated all their thinking; a new paradigm prevails only when the older generation has been "converted" to it, or has died off and been replaced by a new generation. As Kuhn portrays it, a paradigm shift is thus a highly subjective process. He claims that scientific revolutions, like political revolutions, do not employ the normal methods of change.

Now I would have to agree with Kuhn that paradigms are highly resistant to change, but I believe that *observations exert more control* than he admits. An accumulation of anomalies or *ad hoc* adjustments cannot be dismissed indefinitely. I see more overlap than Kuhn does in the observational vocabularies of successive paradigms; in most of his examples there are some common assumptions shared by the competing paradigms. I find more continuity across scientific revolutions than he does; surely many of the prevailing methods as well as earlier data are carried over under the new paradigm. He claims that competing paradigms cannot be rationally adjudicated because the standards of judgment are themselves at issue. I reply that there are criteria common to all the paradigms of modern science—

criteria such as simplicity, coherence, and empirical agreement. These criteria are not paradigm-dependent, though admittedly their application involves considerable subjectivity and historical relativism.

Hopefully this kind of account, which I have sketched all too briefly, could do justice to both *subjective* and *objective* features of science. All data are indeed theory-laden, yet observations do exert a control on theories. Paradigms are indeed resistant to falsification, yet they are not immune to cumulative pressure from discordant data and replacement by alternative paradigms.

IV.   Experience and Interpretation in Religion

Scientific models, then, lead to theories which can be tested against observations. Is there any parallel in religion? Do religious models lead to religious beliefs which can be tested against the data of experience?

To be sure, theory influences data in science. But in religion the inseparability of *data* and *interpretation* is much more problematic. Does the data exercise any control at all on the interpretation? People describe religious experience in conformity with the particular tradition to which they belong. There is a tendency for any set of basic beliefs to produce experiences which can be cited in support of those beliefs. Yet amidst the diversity of world religions there are some family resemblances and common elements, such as the "numinous" and "mystical" strands which Ninian Smart outlines.[23] The mystics of various traditions do seem to describe their experience in similar terms. I would be inclined to say that even the atheist may have the same experience as the theist but interpret it differently. However, I would also have to acknowledge that the atheist's expectations may drastically influence his openness to some kinds of experience.[24]

Basic religious beliefs, I suggest, are more like paradigms than like specific scientific theories. They involve fundamental assumptions and ways of looking at the world. Like paradigms they are highly resistant to falsification, yet the cumulative

weight of evidence does count for or against them and contributes to their eventual modification or abandonment. Religious
beliefs are not invulnerable to change under the pressure of
experience. The *assessment of religious beliefs* is certainly more
debatable than the assessment of scientific paradigms, but the
difference is one of degree. I proposed, against Kuhn, that the
criteria of judgment are independent of particular paradigms,
though their application to the choice of paradigms is very
indirect. Religious beliefs can be judged by similar criteria—
simplicity, systematic coherence, supporting evidence—but the
criteria are vastly more difficult to apply. There will be differences in judgment as to the relative importance of various areas
of experience. Between competing systems of religious belief
there seem to be fewer common assumptions than between
competing scientific paradigms. Religious arguments seem to
be circular—but not totally so if they can be modified under
sufficient weight of conflicting evidence.

What kinds of *evidence* are relevant to the assessment of religious beliefs? I have said that their primary context is the interpretation of moral and religious experience and revelatory
events in the life of communities. Beyond this, religious beliefs
are relevant to other personal and social life situations. The
data to which they direct attention are preeminently the experiences of active selves in decision—in love and hate, joy and
tragedy, life and death, justice and injustice. But religious beliefs also provide a wider interpretive framework; they yield
clues for a coherent view of reality. Frederick Ferré suggests
that religious models serve as "organizing images" with which
we interpret all aspects of experience. The testing of scientific
and religious models are in principle similar, he says, except
that scientific models are used for making predictions:

Barring this one logically inappropriate means of testing the reliability
of models, the metaphors of religion lie open to evaluation along very
similar lines to the models used in the sciences to represent a subject
matter that lies beyond our powers of direct inspection. As organizing
images through which we see ourselves and all things, the powerful
images of religion should bring certain aspects of our experience into
prominence, should minimize the importance of other aspects, and

should throughout function to illuminate our total environment by discovering to us otherwise unnoticed parallelisms, analogies, and patterns among our data.[25]

If religious beliefs do provide a wider interpretive framework, *the problem of evil* must be taken seriously as relevant evidence. Evil does count against traditional theism though it does not falsify it in any simple way. I do not find attempts to justify suffering as character-producing compatible with the extent and depth of human suffering—or with our own vocation to alleviate suffering. I will contend in the next chapter that the idea of divine omnipotence needs to be modified in the light of natural evil, human freedom, and scientific law. My point here is simply that evil is part of the cumulative data to be assessed.

Does *the ambiguity of the evidence* count against theism? Would we not expect God to have revealed himself more clearly? John Hick maintains that, on the contrary, a God who respects human freedom and autonomy would not overwhelm us with indubitable evidence.[26] If God wants our voluntary response, he must safeguard our autonomy and allow for a variety of interpretations of the world, rather than dominating us by revealing himself more directly. He veils himself to protect our independence, and his actions leave room for our uncompelled decision. The assessment of evidence is left up to each individual. There is, of course, another reply to the question of ambiguity: no ultimate organizing image, whether theistic or naturalistic, can be proven or disproven with certainty. Discordant data can always be reconciled by introducing *ad hoc* adjustments. A paradigm is overthrown only by another paradigm; so, too, an ultimate model is displaced only by an alternative ultimate model, not by the data alone.

The view suggested here concerning experience and interpretation would lead to a *confessional theology* closely related to human experience. We can only say: this is what has happened in our lives, and this is how things look from where we stand. Such an approach recognizes the relativism and finitude of every human viewpoint. As H. R. Niebuhr has indicated, self-justification and defensiveness betray the existential stance of faith itself. We need continual self-criticism and doubt, and the acknowledgment that all our formulations are partial and limited.[27]

We must also keep in mind the *other uses of religious models* which have no parallel in science. They serve, I said, to express and evoke dedication to a way of life. They are closely tied to ethics and worship as well as to theology. They influence attitudes and behavior as well as ways of interpreting experience. In many of these functions, vivid religious imagery is more effective than abstract conceptual formulations. In science, a model is related to experience not directly but through articulation in a theory—though I did insist that models also suggest ways in which theoretical terms might be correlated with observation terms. Religious models, however, have a more direct relationship to experience. Especially in these noncognitive functions, models are more influential than articulated beliefs. This is a reflection of the greater personal involvement which religion requires.

V. Conclusions: On the Uses of Models

I have outlined several *similarities* between theoretical models in science and religious models. First, they share certain structural characteristics: both are analogical in origin, extensible to new situations, and comprehensible as units. Second, they have a similar status. Neither is a literal picture of reality, yet neither can be treated as a useful fiction. Models are partial and inadequate ways of imagining what is not observable. They are symbolic representations, for particular purposes, of aspects of reality which are not directly accessible to us. Third, the use of scientific models to order observations has some parallels in the use of religious models to interpret the experience of individuals and communities. Organizing images help us restructure and interpret events in personal life and in the world.

I have also pointed out significant *differences* between religious and scientific models. First, the influence of interpretation on experience is a more serious problem in religion. To be sure, there are no uninterpreted data in science. Yet the control of theory by data is more effective in science than in religion. Second, models in religion are more highly resistant to change, whereas scientific paradigms, though resistant to falsification by data, are not immune to replacement in "scientific revolutions." Third, religious models serve noncognitive functions without parallel in science. While there are diverse types of scientific model used for practical and theoretical purposes, there are distinctive and unique functions of religious models, especially in worship and ethics. Here models evoke and express attitudes and commitments, and their use is valuational and life-orienting.

I have two conclusions to offer from this comparison. On the one hand, the recognition that religious models are not pictures of reality can contribute to *tolerance between religious communities*. In a day when the religions of the world confront each other, the view proposed here might engender humility and tentativeness in claims made on behalf of any model. One facet of secularity which we can welcome is its acceptance of religious pluralism. In place of exclusive claims of finality, we can acknowledge the possibility of a variety of significant religious models, without lapsing into a complete relativism which would undercut all concern for truth.

The second conclusion is that the common stereotype of *science as objective* and *religion as subjective* is untenable. Scientific models are products of creative and analogical imagination. Man the knower plays a crucial role throughout science: data are theory-laden, paradigms are resistant to falsification. In religion each of these subjective features is more prominent: the use of a plurality of models, the influence of interpretation on data, the resistance of basic presuppositions to falsification. But at each of these points I see between science and religion a difference of degree rather than an absolute contrast.

If this analysis is correct, *the challenge of the scientific method* to religion can be met by a more adequate understanding of the character of both science and religion. There are, moreover, distinctive noncognitive functions of religious models which, as we shall see in later chapters, are all the more important in a technological age. We cannot dismiss religion in the name of science. The obituary from which I started was premature. Whoever that was who died, I suspect that he was an imposter.

CHAPTER TWO

The Autonomy of Nature

The movement beginning about the thirteenth century towards the autonomy of man (under which head I place the discovery of the laws by which the world lives and manages in science, social and political affairs, art, ethics and religion) has in our time reached a certain completion. Man has learned to cope with all questions of importance without recourse to God as a working hypothesis. . . . So our coming of age forces us to a true recognition of our situation *vis à vis* God. God is teaching us that we must live as men who can get along very well without him.

Dietrich Bonhoeffer, *Letters and Papers from Prison*

To the scientist, nature is a self-contained order in which purely natural forces rather than transcendent powers are operative. The world seems to be governed by orderly scientific laws which leave no room for the activity of God. This is secularity, not in the sense of intellectual autonomy, but in the assumption of the autonomy of nature. The issues here are more theological than philosophical. How can God act if the world is governed by scientific laws?

I will indicate the responses to this challenge given by Catholic and Protestant traditionalists, by existentialist theologians,

and by linguistic analysts. Then I will explore the direction
taken by process theology, especially its evolutionary view of
nature and its proposal of a model of God based on divine
persuasion rather than on divine omnipotence. Here are introduced a number of themes which are developed further in
subsequent chapters: the openness of the future (and the concomitant rejection of both scientific and theological determinism), the interdependence of all beings, the freedom of man,
and an affirmation of the world which is consistent with a Christian secularity. It will be suggested also that the absence of an
adequate theology of nature, and the presence of a false dichotomy between man and nature, have contributed to the exploitative attitudes toward the natural world which are at the
root of our present ecological crisis.

I.   The Challenge to Orthodoxy

Let me begin by indicating how the problem arose. Classical
theism had asserted *God's sovereign control of nature.* The biblical
story of God's mighty acts was elaborated into the doctrines of
divine omnipotence and predestination. God, it was said, governs and rules the world in his providential wisdom. He is free
to carry out his purposes; all events are totally subordinate to
his will. Divine foreordination was said to involve not only fore-
knowledge but also predetermination of every event. Both Me-
dieval Thomism and Reformation Protestantism held that God
intervenes as a direct cause of particular events, in addition to
his more usual action working through secondary natural
causes. This aspect of the orthodox doctrines of creation and
providence might be represented by the model of the potter
and the clay.

But with the rise of modern science in the seventeenth century, nature was increasingly viewed as *a law-abiding machine.*
God was the divine clockmaker and the world was the clock—
an autonomous and self-sufficient mechanism. Newton's contemporary, Robert Boyle, started by defending God's freedom
and sovereignty, but ended by asserting that God in his wisdom
has planned things so that he does not have to intervene. The

unfailing rule of law, not miraculous intervention, is the evidence of his benevolence. Providence is expressed not in particular events but in the total cosmic design, the over-all structure and order of the world. This was the inactive God of Deism, who started the mechanism and then let it run by itself. The dominant model of God's relation to nature was the clockmaker and the clock.

Yet there continued to be various *gaps in the scientific account* in which God could be invoked. Newton held that there are irregularities in the solar system which would build up if God did not step in periodically to correct them. The cosmic clock had to be reset, as it were. In the next century Laplace proved that the irregularities would correct themselves; concerning God's role in planetary motion he could rightly say: "I have no need of that hypothesis." A century later Darwin showed that one does not need God as a hypothesis to account for the origin of man. One of the last gaps, that between the nonliving and the living, has been almost closed within the past decade. The "God of the gaps," invoked to explain unexplained facts, retreated further as each gap in human knowledge disappeared. God's special action as a cause, producing effects on the same level as natural events, was replaced by law-obeying natural causes in each area of scientific advance.

Today nature is viewed in its totality as *a lawful and autonomous order.* Plagues and earthquakes are taken as natural events, not as acts of divine retribution. Only by excluding reference to the supernatural can we predict and control the world—and travel to the moon. Scientific explanations satisfy us and we do not feel the need to look further. Scientific laws state regularities which, we are confident, will continue to prevail. Events are for us not isolated occurrences but parts of an interconnected web, a continuous and unified whole. Nature is a self-contained system whose interactions are to be exhaustively accounted for in purely natural terms by lawful cause-and-effect relationships.

In the face of this picture of nature, some theologians have insisted that *God works through natural forces.* Neo-Thomist Catholics and neo-orthodox Protestants have reemphasized one component of classical thought, namely, the idea that God as *primary cause* uses *secondary causes* to effect his will. Thus Karl Barth defends God's omnipotence and control but insists that divine action as primary cause is on a totally different level from the natural causes which he employs. When a man uses a pen to write a letter, both man and pen are causes, but the instrument is subordinate to the purposes of the man. Similarly natural forces are subordinate to God's absolute control; he can use scientific laws without violating them. He remains the sovereign ruler of nature. In Barth's words, "God rules unconditionally and irresistibly in all occurrences." "All creaturely determination is wholly and utterly at the disposal of his power."[1]

Contemporary Neo-Thomists stress the ideas of *divine conservation and concurrence.* God sustains and upholds the created order and the structures he has ordained. The world is lawful because each being has its essence, its intrinsic nature; God provides it with a natural inclination which is genuinely its own but which also expresses the divine purposes. Everything is allowed for in the original blueprint and no further revisions are needed to accomplish his will. Divine omnipotence is exercised through *predestination.* God foreknows all future events and establishes them in his eternal decree. Note the view of time which is implied here—time as the unrolling of a scroll on which all things are already written. God in his timeless omniscience knows the future and predetermines its course.[2]

In this view, *the cosmic design* is built into the structures of nature. Before Darwin it was assumed that each kind of creature was designed and created once-and-for-all in its present form. Since Darwin, design was ascribed to the whole system of laws through which evolution occurred. Purpose is displayed by a universe whose processes could bring forth life and personality. The revised "argument from design" focuses attention on the various conditions favorable to life, the chemical and physical properties on which life depends, the coordination of successive levels of organization. God's role was to program the laws of the world according to a preconceived plan. Design was built into the structure which achieves his purposes. God rules through the rule of law. Here was a way to acknowledge both divine sovereignty and a lawful world.

But notice that if this approach is adopted, it means that *God does not act in nature* except to sustain its general structure. He is not actively related to particular events. We are back to the God of Deism. Notice, moreover, that this approach embodies *deterministic* assumptions. There are no genuine alternatives if God foreordains all events through an initial plan of inflexible laws. I will later suggest that evolution is unpredictable and that there are spontaneity and novelty in the history of nature. The Newtonian analogy of the world as a clock-like mechanism no longer seems adequate. A mechanical world, to which neither man nor God is intimately related, becomes an object for human manipulation and exploitation.

A further objection to the doctrine of *divine omnipotence,* in both classical and modern versions, is that it makes God responsible for *evil and suffering.* If all events are foreordained by God, is he not, inescapably, the author of evil? Attempts to minimize the reality of evil are not convincing to most people today. In Albert Camus' novel, *The Plague,* Father Paneloux is watching a child die of the plague. "Perhaps," he says, "we should love what we cannot understand." The doctor, Rieux, replies: "No, Father. I've a very different idea of love. And until my dying day I shall refuse to love a scheme of things in which children are put to torture." Rieux, speaking for Camus, would rather have no God than an omnipotent God responsible for human suffering.

I would argue that divine omnipotence is also incompatible with *human freedom,* though valiant efforts have been made throughout the history of theology to escape this conclusion. It is in the name of human responsibility that Thomas Altizer wants us to will the death of the authoritarian God who keeps man submissive and dependent.[3] Supernaturalism has too often seemed to repress the natural, rather than to fulfill it. God has too often been cast as the enemy of man's freedom and maturity. Thus both the autonomy of nature and the autonomy of man have been strong challenges to the idea of an omnipotent deity. I want to examine three responses to this challenge: the *existentialist retreat* to the realm of interiority; the *linguistic solution* which distinguishes alternative languages; and *process thought,* which represents God as a noncoercive participant in the cosmic process.

II. The Existentialist Retreat

The retreat of religion from nature to *the realm of man's inwardness* started with Kant. Kant drew a sharp line between the realm of theoretical reason (the deterministic patterns of the phenomenal world, which are the concern of science) and the realm of practical reason (the decisions of free moral selves, which he saw as the ground of religion). He held that the recognition of moral obligation is the only legitimate basis of religious beliefs. Following Kant, Romanticism stressed the religious significance of moral and spiritual consciousness. The dichotomy between history and nature developed further in Ritschl and other nineteenth century Protestants. Man was set over against nature. History was said to be religiously significant as the arena of free personal selves, in contrast to the lawful and impersonal order of nature.

It is often said that the biblical God acts primarily in history rather than in nature. But today *the secular understanding of history* is as prevalent as the secular understanding of nature. The historian is as reluctant as the scientist to invoke supernatural causes. He accounts for events in terms of natural causes, human decisions, and social forces, not divine providence. Consequently, most contemporary theologians acknowledge that the action of God is seen only by the eye of faith; we must talk not about the events themselves but about the way the religious community interpreted those events. In the Exodus narrative, the strong east wind, which allowed Moses and his followers to escape from Egypt, can be understood as a natural phenomenon, but Israel interpreted it as a providential deliverance. As Langdon Gilkey points out, we end by studying Hebrew faith, not God's mighty acts. If God acted at all, it was in the inward inciting of man's response, rather than in either nature or history.[4]

Religious existentialism pushes even further the contrast between the sphere of *personal selfhood* and the sphere of *impersonal objects*. In Martin Buber's terminology, *I-Thou* relationships are characterized by total involvement and participation of the whole self, by directness and immediacy of apprehension, by the reciprocity and openness of true dialogue, and by awareness, sensitivity, and availability. *I-It* relationships, on the other hand, are characterized by detached analysis, manipulative control, practical utilization.[5] Religion requires *I-Thou* attitudes of immediacy and personal involvement, while science exemplifies the analytic detachment of the *I-It*. Here we have a total contrast between personal subjectivity and impersonal objectivity.

Rudolf Bultmann has been the most influential exponent of the proposition that God does not act in the objective arena of nature but in *man's existential self-understanding*. He considers nature to be a rigidly determined mechanical order. He maintains that the scientific view of the universe as a completely closed system of causal laws excludes any belief in God's action in the world. Bultmann holds that it is theologically as well as scientifically dubious to imagine that God produces changes in the world. The transcendent is falsely objectified when it is spoken of in the language of space and time or pictured as a supernatural cause. To Bultmann a *myth* is a misrepresentation of divine activity as if it were an objective occurrence. But rather than rejecting the mythical elements of the Bible, as earlier liberals did, he wants us to recover their deeper meaning by translating them back into the language of personal experience, which was their real meaning all along.[6]

Bultmann urges us to "demythologize" statements about God's activity in nature, that is, to reinterpret them existentially in terms of *man's self-understanding*. The key question is always: what does the mythical imagery say about my personal existence and my relationship to God now? The Christian message always refers to new possibilities for my life—decision, rebirth, realization of authentic human life; it isn't really concerned about observable events in the external world apart from my involvement. The doctrine of creation, for example, is not a neutral statement about cosmological origins, but an individual confession of present dependence on God: "The Lord is *my* creator!" "In gratitude I receive my life as a gift." All religious formulations must be statements about a new understanding of personal existence, not about objective occurrences in the world.

For Bultmann, then, providence is a doctrine concerning not God's activity in nature but *how one looks at natural events*. He writes as follows:

> In faith I can understand an accident with which I meet as a gracious gift of God, or as his punishment, or as his chastisement. On the other hand, I can understand the same accident as a link in the chain of the natural course of events. If, for example, my child has recovered from a dangerous illness, I give thanks because he has saved my child. . . . This is the paradox of faith, that faith "nevertheless" understands as God's action here and now an event which is completely intelligible in the natural or historical connection of events.[7]

Faith, Bultmann implies, makes a difference only in how one takes an outcome which was itself determined by inexorable causal laws. The cosmic clock continues on its own. In effect, the existentialists assign nature to the scientist and confine religion to man's inward life. Nature, with its lawful, impersonal order, is abandoned as a sphere of God's activity. God acts only in the realm of selfhood. He is Lord not over nature but in the hearts of the faithful.

The existentialist approach thus seems to provide a ready solution to the challenge of *the autonomy of nature*. Science and religion each have their distinctive domains which are mutually exclusive, isolated from each other in watertight compartments. The idea of divine omnipotence over nature is abandoned, and the problems of natural evil and human freedom, which were so acute for both classical and modern orthodoxy, are put to one side. Despite these advantages, several major objections must be raised.

First, existentialism, like Neo-Thomism and neo-orthodoxy, perpetuates *an inadequate view of nature*. Today we do not have to accept the Newtonian picture of the world as a mechanically determined causal system. I will discuss the new view of nature when I come to process thought below.

Second, existentialism draws an absolute contrast between the *objectivity* of science and the *subjectivity* of religion. In the previous chapter I tried to show that there were subjective and objective factors in both fields, though in differing proportions. But the existentialist ends with a subjective account of religion. God acts in our interpretation of events, not in the events themselves. Confrontation with nature and history is merely the occasion of personal reorientation. God's acts are transactions in the life of the believer, the present transformation of man's outlook. I would grant that God is not encountered apart from personal involvement, but I would not grant that God's action is limited to the sphere of selfhood. We will find that according to process thought God makes a difference in events, not just in our way of looking at events.

Third, any *sharp separation of man and nature* appears dubious today. Evolutionary biology, ecology, and biochemistry have all shown us ways in which man is part of nature—as process thought recognizes. Nature has a history, and human history is conditioned by nature. Moreover, man's inner life is as much subject to natural explanations as are events in the world. The psychologist joins the scientist and the historian in seeking an account which makes no reference to God. The very same problems concerning the relation of divine action and natural cause, which arose in thinking about nature, arise again in the realm of selfhood to which the existentialist has retreated.

Fourth, if Christianity is radically interiorized, *nature is left devoid of meaning.* To existentialism, the world is the impersonal stage for the drama of personal existence. Are the long stretches of cosmic history before man's appearance then unrelated to God? Is nature only an object to be exploited for man's benefit? Surely the biblical view sees more continuity between nature and grace. It portrays a single creative-redemptive work. The natural world is part of the drama, not a mere setting for it. We need a theology of nature as well as of human existence. At this point also I see considerable promise in process theology.

III. The Linguistic Solution

Before considering process views, let me outline the linguistic proposals which might seem to offer a way out of our dilemma. In Chapter One I noted some of the distinctive noncognitive functions of religious language. *Religious language* is used to express and evoke self-commitment, to recommend a way of life, to endorse a set of moral principles, and to engender particular attitudes toward the world. Thus statements about *providence* could be understood as personal confessions that the pattern of events has significance for one's own life. The idea of providence would be a useful fiction, a way of looking at and responding to events *as if* they were from the hand of God. In this view, the function of the idea is not to offer an explanation of events in the world, but to change our attitudes toward events. We don't ask about its truth or falsity but about its usefulness in human life. To regard the world as purposeful is to respond to it in distinctive ways.

Up to this point the linguistic solution resembles the existentialist retreat to interiority. But some language analysts go a step further and include *cognitive* as well as *noncognitive* functions. They claim that the doctrine of providence provides not only a framework of life-orientation but also a perspective on the world, an interpretive scheme for understanding cosmic history. Some features of the pattern of events stand out more clearly if one sees them as part of the divine purpose. These language analysts talk about God's relation to nature, and not just to selfhood. The contrast between man and nature is avoided, and attention is directed instead to the diverse functions of language.[8]

Moreover, linguistic analysts differ from existentialists in their view of *scientific laws.* They usually adopt the positivist thesis that theories are not pictures of reality but calculating devices for making predictions, or perhaps technical tools for controlling the world. The so-called "laws of nature" are mental constructs, useful fictions for correlating observations. Whereas the existentialists take nature to be mechanistic and deterministic, most linguistic analysts try to avoid making statements about nature. For them determinism is simply a useful strategy to guide the work of the scientist; it is not a universal truth about the world.[9] If the scientist follows the maxim that "every event has a cause," he will search for regularities and will be more likely to achieve his goals of prediction and control. Causality is not a question of necessary connections between events; it is, as Hume maintained, just a human habit of regular association of phenomena.

According to the linguistic approach, every community of language users is *selective in its interests*. Every discipline develops its own symbolic language and replaces the total situation by a model serving its particular purposes. The scientist is interested in regularities among phenomena; he selects not according to the importance of a problem but according to its tractability to his methods. Therefore, he cannot claim to give a complete account. Think of Eddington's parable about the zoologist, studying deep-sea life by means of a net of ropes on a two-inch mesh, who after repeated expeditions concluded that there are no fish smaller than two inches in the sea! Our methods always limit what we find. Men ask diverse types of questions arising from a diversity of purposes in inquiry; the scientist, in particular, asks very specialized kinds of questions.

This approach leads one, then, to welcome *alternative languages* for dealing with any one domain. There can be a variety of modes of analyzing a given system, using a variety of models and conceptual schemes. There can be several levels of analysis which are not mutually exclusive. For example, explanations in terms of *causes* and explanations in terms of *goals* may both be useful. In the past, scientists reacted violently against the idea of purpose because it seemed to undercut the search for lawful regularities. Today it is widely recognized that purpose and mechanism are alternative ways of regarding a system. Goal-directed behavior is characterized by flexibility of response to changing conditions, and the response is describable in relation to an end-state not yet achieved. Present changes are analyzed as phases of a pattern covering a span of time. But the same system can be described in terms of mechanical causes. Each account is complete and without gaps, on its own level, and neither account precludes the other. Purpose and mechanism are not an "either-or" dichotomy, but alternative analyses useful in differing contexts of inquiry.

I find some of the recent linguistic writings about human action helpful in suggesting a possible model for God's action. What is an *action?* It is a succession of events ordered toward an end. Its unity consists in an intention to realize a goal. An act can be analyzed into subacts, each unified toward achieving a subgoal; hammering a nail is a subact of building a house. An act is different from a bodily movement. A given bodily movement (for example, moving my arm outward in a particular way) may perform various acts (mailing letters, sowing seeds, dealing cards, etc.). An action cannot be specified by any finite set of bodily movements, but only by its purpose or intent.[10]

Analysis in terms of *intentions* does not preclude analysis in terms of physiological laws. The physiologist need not refer to my purposes when he explains my arm movement. Moreover, intentions are never directly observable. An action may be difficult to identify without a larger context. Calling it an action involves an interpretation of its meaning, which often depends on observation over a considerable temporal span. It may, of course, be misinterpreted and wrongly identified. The important point is that the unity is one of intentionality rather than of causality. The agent transcends any single action, and is never fully expressed in any series of actions.

Now the language of human action can provide a model for talking about *divine action.* Suppose we look on the whole course of cosmic history as God's master act to achieve his purposes. All nature and history are one all-encompassing act unified by his intentions. As Gordon Kaufman suggests, there are various subacts—the emergence of life, the advent of man, the growth of culture—within the total action moving toward greater consciousness, freedom, and community. The history of Israel and the life of Christ would represent subacts further particularizing the divine purpose.[11]

Divine intentions do not enter the scientific account of cosmic history, any more than human intentions enter the physiological account of an arm movement. Purpose is at best difficult to discern when we see only a small portion of the total action. A religious tradition gives us a vision of the wider context within which we interpret the pattern. We cannot claim to start from uninterpreted pure data; we see the world from a historically conditioned perspective. God is not fully expressed in historical action, even as a human agent transcends his particular actions. In short, the language of human action would encourage us to treat the language of divine action as an alternative to scientific language, not a competitor with it. It would provide a model of *God as agent,* stressing intentionality rather than causality. The relation of a human agent to his acts is taken as an analogy for the relation of God to cosmic history.

This is an attractive solution to our dilemma concerning God and nature. Yet I wonder whether we can really leave the matter there. Even in the case of human action, don't we have to press further to ask how *the language of action* and *the language of causality* are related to each other? Don't we have to elaborate some concept of selfhood and its relation to the body? Having done this, would we want to use the relation of self to body as a model for God's relation to the world? Is the world God's body, as it were? Or should we defend interpersonal analogies which allow both God and the world greater independence from each other? If we say that all cosmic history is God's act, have we not once again ruled out human freedom and made God responsible for evil? To avoid making God the sole agent of everything that happens, we need a model in which more than one agent influences a given event. It is precisely such a model which process thought provides.

There is also a more basic objection. Most linguistic analysts think of alternative languages as instruments employed for particular purposes, rather than as descriptions of reality. But I maintained in the preceding chapter that both scientist and theologian *use language more realistically* and neither will settle for useful fictions. Both make truth claims which are to be judged true or false, not simply useful. Even if many of the functions of the two fields differ, the cognitive functions of both will contribute to an understanding of reality. If there are alternative languages about a single world, they cannot be totally un-related. We have to ask how our interactions with nature, man, and God give rise to these diverse languages. We must seek a unified view of the world and a coherent interpretation of all experience.

In my opinion, the attempts of existentialism and linguistic analysis to avoid *metaphysics* do not succeed. The scientist and the theologian inevitably make metaphysical assumptions, whether they intend to or not. The quest for unity drives us to articulate a coherent and comprehensive set of categories in terms of which every element in experience can be interpreted. Any attempt to relate science and religion in general, or to discuss the relation of nature to God in particular, will eventually require reflection on the structures of the world. True, there are dangers that an attempted synthesis of the two fields will distort one or the other by imposing alien categories which threaten its integrity. But if we are aware of these dangers, we can learn much from process thought, the only major metaphysical system developed in the twentieth century which deliberately tried to take both science and religion into account.

IV.   Process Theology

Let us consider, then, the contribution of Alfred North White-head and his more recent interpreters.[12] I will suggest that, as a model of God's relation to the world, process thinkers use neither the potter and the clay, nor the clockmaker and the clock, nor the agent and his acts, but a basically *interpersonal analogy*. To show this, it is necessary to summarize the basic concepts of Whitehead's system—in as simple language as possible.

Whitehead starts with a set of very general categories which with suitable modifications can be applied to all kinds of entity. He thinks of every entity as a series of momentary events, each of which is to be considered as a moment of experience that takes account of other events and responds to them. Built into the most fundamental concepts of Whiteheadian metaphysics are the ideas of *interdependence* and *the openness of the future* (the existence of alternative potentialities and the rejection of determinism).

Causality, in Whiteheadian thought, is a complex process in which three strands are interwoven. Every new event is in part the product of *efficient causation,* that is, the influence of previous occurrences upon it. Each moment of experience receives objective "data" from its past, but it can conform to that past in more than one way. There is thus an element of *self-causation* or self-creation, since every event unifies what is given to it from the past in its own manner from its unique perspective on the world. It contributes something of its own in the way it appropriates its past, relates itself to various possibilities, and produces a novel synthesis that is not strictly deducible from its antecedents. There is a creative selection from among alternative potentialities in terms of goals and aims, which is *final causation*. Every new occurrence can, in short, be looked on as a present response to past events in terms of potentialities grasped.

Now Whitehead ascribes the ordering of these potentialities to God. God as the *primordial ground of order* structures the potential forms of relationship before they are actualized. In this function God seems to be an abstract and impersonal metaphysical principle. But Whitehead's God also has specific purposes for the realization of maximum value. He selects particular possibilities for particular entities. He is *the ground of novelty* as well as of order. He presents new possibilities, among which there are alternatives left open. He elicits the self-creation of individual entities and thereby allows for freedom as well as structure. By valuing particular potentialities to which creatures respond, God influences the world without determining it. God acts by being experienced by the world, affecting the constitution of successive moments. His vision of ideal possibilities for particular situations changes the world. But he never determines the outcome of events or violates the self-creation of each being. Every event is the joint product of past causes, divine purposes, and the emerging entity's own action toward the future.

I would suggest that, in process thought, God's relation to

every being is not unlike *a father's relation to his children.* The basic
model is not the potter's coercive power over the clay, but the
wise parent's loving concern for the growing child. A parent
cannot compel a child to learn; his educational effect depends
on the love and respect he elicits and the ideals which he holds
up to the child. God's power likewise is the power of *persuasion*
rather than of *coercion,* of love rather than of compulsion. It is
the lure of ideals which must be actualized by other beings.
Whitehead rejects the image of God as the omnipotent mon-
arch, the imperial ruler, in favor of what he calls "the Galilean
vision of humility," the idea of God as "the fellow-sufferer who
understands."[13] In a similar vein, Bonhoeffer wrote: "God allows himself to be edged out of the world and onto the cross.
God is weak and powerless, and that is exactly the way, the only
way, in which he can be with us and help us."[14] The cross shows
us a distinctive kind of power, the power of a love which accepts
suffering. These are biblical ideas of which classical orthodoxy
tended to lose sight.

Love always acts by *evoking a free response.* The unique power
of love is its ability to evoke a response while respecting the
integrity of the other. In the Whiteheadian scheme every entity
must respond for itself, and nothing that happens is God's act
alone. God does not act directly but rather influences the creatures to act. Each entity has considerable independence and its
response is genuinely its own. If I respond to God, the response
is mine alone, not the product of irresistible grace; in the last
analysis I must decide for myself. Process thinkers reject not
only *omnipotence* but also *predestination.* If there is genuine freedom and novelty in the world, then even God cannot know the
future until the decisions have been made by individual agents.
Time is not the unrolling of a scroll on which everything is
already recorded, but an ongoing process in which alternative
possibilities are open until choices are made at a plurality of
centers of responsibility. God interacts with the world in time,
rather than determining it in his eternal decree. He respects the
freedom of his creatures.

For Whitehead, God's action is *the evocation of response.* Since
man's capacity for response far exceeds that of other beings, it

is in human life that God's creative influence can be most effective—or can be most willfully opposed. God's ability to engender creative change in lower beings seems to be very limited. He is always one factor among many, and particularly with respect to low-level beings, in which experience is rudimentary and creativity is minimal, his power seems to be negligible. Insofar as natural agents exercise causal efficacy, God's ability to compel change is thereby restricted. But we must remember that God is not absent from events that monotonously repeat their past, for he is the ground of order. God's purpose for low-level beings is just for them to be orderly; his gift is the structure of the possibilities they exemplify. At such levels God's novel action may be beyond detection—though perhaps in cosmic history and emergent evolution there are signs of his creativity in the inanimate. Even when God does contribute to novelty he always acts along with other causes, qualifying but not abrogating their operation. We can never extricate the "acts of God" from their involvement in the complex of natural processes through which he works.

But does it make sense to think of *God's relation to lower organisms* as even remotely similar to God's relation to man? In order to give a unified account of the world, Whitehead employs categories which in very attenuated forms can be said to characterize simple beings, but which at the same time have at least some resemblance to our own awareness as experiencing subjects. This procedure is a product of several convictions: that metaphysics is the elaboration of a set of general categories applicable to all events; that the universe is continuous and interrelated; and that human experience is the one aspect of reality that we know directly. He treats lower levels as simpler cases of complex experience, rather than trying to interpret higher levels by concepts derived from the inanimate world. There is a continuous spectrum of complexity in organisms from man down to the amoeba and beyond, and one cannot set any absolute limits to the range of applicability of any particular category. Human experience is an extreme instance of an event in nature, and hence is taken to exhibit the generic features of all experience.

There is, moreover, considerable support from science for *the view of nature* endorsed by process thinkers. In the Newtonian view, which prevailed until the last century, nature was essentially *static,* with all things presumed to have been created in their present forms. Nature was *simple*—reducible, that is, to a few types of entity governed by a few basic laws. Nature was *deterministic,* its future in principle predictable from knowledge of its present. The model of clock and clockmaker seemed entirely appropriate. We have seen that neo-orthodoxy and existentialism tend to perpetuate this image of the world as a machine.

But today it appears that nature is neither static, simple, or determined. It is a *dynamic* process of becoming, always changing and developing, radically temporal in character. This is an incomplete cosmos still coming into being. Again, it is not simple but highly *complex.* The world is many-leveled; it includes many types of entity and many types of law not reducible to each other. Process thinkers are critical of reductionism, and hold that an organism is an integral system with a hierarchy of levels of organization. Then again, nature is not determined but *unpredictable.* Many scientific laws are statistical and do not allow prediction of individual events. To the epistemological realist, the Heisenberg Uncertainty Principle implies that indeterminacy is a feature of nature itself and not merely a limitation in human knowledge. In Heisenberg's own words, in quantum physics "the concept of potentiality has been restored."[15]

These three characteristics—dynamism, complexity, and unpredictability—are particularly prominent in recent writing on *evolution.* Dobzhansky views evolution as a creative process whose outcome is not predictable because gene recombinations and mutations are unrepeatable events producing unique individuals.[16] Of the billions of potential patterns of genes that an offspring of given parents might have, only one is realized. G. G. Simpson and Ernst Mayr see evolution as unrepeatable because unique chains of contingent historical circumstances, environmental changes, and the competition of particular species will never occur again.[17] They conclude that if there is life on other planets there is no reason to expect it even remotely to resemble life on earth. Novelty has occurred throughout the past; the future is open and unknown. Moreover, Alister Hardy and others have shown the importance of the organism's internal drives and activities in evolutionary history. A new development can be initiated, not just by genetic or environmental changes, but by the organism's own patterns of novel activity, which are later aided by mutations favorable to them.[18]

A forceful expression of the evolutionary outlook has been given by the Jesuit paleontologist, Teilhard de Chardin. Teilhard portrays vividly the temporality and organic interdependence of the ongoing cosmic process.[19] Like Whitehead he stresses the continuity of levels of reality, though he speaks of thresholds and critical points at which new phenomena appear: life, reflective thought, society. He pictures *"the within of things"* as an elementary kind of responsiveness and sensitivity in even the simplest creatures, a forerunner of man's mental life, an interiority reaching all the way down the scale of life until it becomes "imperceptible and lost in darkness as we trace it back." Each level has its roots in earlier levels and represents the flowering of what was potentially present all along. The higher was already in the lower in rudimentary form.

Teilhard, like Whitehead, holds that God is actively involved in the *continuing creation* of a world which is still coming into being. He avoids postulating intervention at specific points, and instead emphasizes God's creativity immanent throughout the cosmic process. Though he sometimes refers to God as primary cause working through lawful secondary causes, he usually suggests a more active role: God "animates" the world and "leads" it to fulfillment. Man and nature collaborate with God in bringing the cosmos to completion. The world's maturation is a precondition of the final consummation. However, Teilhard does not develop his informal process metaphysics systematically or discuss how lawfulness, spontaneity, and divine influence are related. His writing is more poetic than analytical, and his forceful metaphors and imaginative analogies are vivid but often vague.[20] Teilhard's mystical intensity and his dramatic vision of a dynamic and unified cosmos are indeed impressive, but it is up to others to give his suggestive ideas a more precise philosophical expression.

V. Conclusions: On God and Nature

I have traced the dominance of successive models in representing God's relation to nature: the potter and the clay in orthodoxy, the clockmaker and the clock in Deism (and also in neo-orthodoxy and existentialism), the agent and his acts in linguistic analysis, and finally the father and the child in process thought. I will conclude by indicating what seem to me to be the main strengths and weaknesses of process thought concerning God and nature. On the one side, I see three very positive contributions:

1. Process thought yields a theology of nature. To neo-orthodoxy, nature is the unredeemed setting for man's redemption. To existentialism, nature is the impersonal stage for the drama of personal existence. But to process thought, nature is part of the drama of a single creative-redemptive work in which God and the world both participate. Process thinkers seek a unified and coherent world view, in contrast to the plurality of unrelated languages with which linguistic analysis leaves us. They try to develop an inclusive conceptual scheme for interpreting all areas of experience, rather than a succession of useful fictions for specialized purposes. They reject any dichotomy which would assign nature to science and man's inner life or attitudes to religion; they stress man's unity with nature and the interdependence of all life. By emphasizing divine immanence they encourage respect for nature, which is a valuable corrective to our ruthlessness in plundering the earth. Such a theology of nature could make a major contribution to the development of an ecological conscience.

2. Process thought illuminates the problem of evil. If the classical ideas of omnipotence and predestination are given up, God is exonerated of responsibility for natural evil. If no event is the product of God's agency alone, he works with a world, given to him in every moment, which never fully embodies his will. The creatures, and above all man, are free to reject the higher vision. Suffering is inevitable in a world of beings with conflicting goals. Pain is part of the price of consciousness and intensity of feeling. In an evolutionary world, struggle is integral to the realization of greater values. As Teilhard wrote, evil is intrinsic to an evolving cosmos as it would not be to an instantaneous creation. Suffering and death are not punishments for sin but structural concomitants of what he called "the immense travail" of a world in birth.

3. Process thought encourages affirmation of the world. Time, history, and nature are taken seriously. Here is an orientation toward the future, an openness to new possibilities. Evolution continues; God calls us forward to love, freedom, and creativity. Too often in the past we have viewed God as the authoritarian judge, the represser of human vitalities. Now we can see him as the fulfiller of man, evoking our capacities for a more fully human existence. Our own responsibility is enhanced if we believe that God does nothing by himself. We are called to be co-creators in an unfinished universe, participants in God's work. Man's freedom and dignity are affirmed without denying his unity with nature. Against all dualisms of spirit versus matter or mind versus body, process thinkers defend the unity and value of man as a total being. Man is essentially continuous with nature, rather than discontinuous as neo-orthodoxy and existentialism assume. All these factors lead Whitehead, Teilhard, and their followers to a keen appreciation of the positive values of secularity and involvement in the world—topics which I will discuss in the next chapter.

Process thought, then, contributes a theology of nature, illumination of the problem of evil, and an affirmative attitude toward the world. But it also presents a number of problems and difficulties. A complaint which might have been valid a decade ago is the sheer difficulty of understanding Whitehead's abstract and technical writing. Today, however, there are very readable presentations of Whiteheadian thought by John Cobb, Eugene Peters, Peter Hamilton, Norman Pittenger, and others.[21] But there are four continuing problems which I will put as questions:

1. Does process thought compromise the autonomy of nature? It seems to offer a new version of "the God of the gaps"—positing many infinitesimal gaps in the natural order, instead of the few big ones around which past conflicts of science and religion centered. But doesn't even this more limited role of God's activity run counter to the modern assumption of the autonomy of nature? Isn't God's influence—whether large or small, sudden or gradual, coercive or persuasive—ruled out by the demand for scientific explanation in terms of natural causes alone? Aren't we forced to return to the neo-classical idea of a strictly gapless chain of secondary causes, or to the linguistic view of a gapless scientific account?

I think I would reply as follows. If by the *autonomy of nature* you mean the exclusion of divine activity, then you have of course by definition already denied any continuing role for God. If, however, autonomy refers to the partial independence of every being and the lawfulness of nature, then the process scheme is not ruled out. For process thinkers insist that each being's response to God is genuinely its own act, not God's; creaturely independence is protected here. Moreover, these authors try to do justice to the lawfulness of nature—but also to the element of unpredictability at various levels (from quantum atom to evolutionary mutation to human freedom). They also agree with the linguistic analysts that scientific laws are always selective and abstractive. Thus the "gaps" in the Whiteheadian account are very different from those invoked in earlier centuries. God has a clearly defined role here, but his contribution can never be separated out because he always acts with other causes. He does not intervene intermittently from outside, for he is already present in the unfolding of every event.

2. Does process thought compromise God's sovereignty? In the orthodox view of omnipotence, an impersonal model of power as coercion is implicit. The coercive model can represent God's sovereignty over stones, but in representing sovereignty over people it jeopardizes human freedom. Existentialism, on the other hand, seems to end by denying God any influence on nature apart from man. Process philosophy comes out in between: it rejects absolute sovereignty, but defends divine influence on the world. Its problem is just the reverse of orthodox-y's. A personal model of divine power—as love, persuasion, and the evocation of response—fits God's relation to people, but it seems to leave him powerless over stones, whose capacity for novel response is negligible. Doesn't this deny God's sovereignty over nature?

A possible reply might run as follows. God apparently doesn't do very much with stones, except to maintain them in their stability. In Whiteheadian terms, a stone is a mere aggregate; it has no organized structure and is not the scene of any unified experience at all. But even the simplest cell does have an organic unity and an infinitesimal responsiveness and spontaneity. Its openness to new potentialities is small, and is disclosed only in the long ages of cosmic history. This may offer very little for God to work with, but it seems to be the way things are constituted. After all, it took two billion years for God to create an animal from the primeval soup. After that, things could move more rapidly; the transition from ape to man spans less than a million years. And it is human life which provides the greatest opportunities for God's influence today; the potentialities for rapid change are far greater than ever before. The face of the earth can be altered in the span of a century or less. As existentialism recognizes, human existence is now the most important locus of divine activity. Yet we don't have to deny totally God's influence on the rest of nature.

3. *Does process thought neglect the primary functions of religious language?* I suggested in the preceding chapter that religious beliefs arise in the interpretation of individual religious experience and corporate history. The context of religious discourse is the worshiping community. Existentialists rightly insist on the necessity of personal involvement. Linguistic analysts rightly stress the distinctive noncognitive functions of religious language—self-commitment, life-orientation, endorsement of attitudes. Process thought, by contrast, is often abstract and speculative. The God of metaphysics serves quite different functions from the God of worship. Philosophical and ontological categories begin to replace the historical and personal categories of the Bible.

I would say that these are real dangers in process thought, but that one can guard against them. One can recognize the primary noncognitive functions of religious language but also acknowledge cognitive functions involving assertions about reality. One can use the classical language of salvation, yet metaphysics is inescapable in discussing God's relation to nature. Process thought can contribute to a *theology of nature*—that is, an attempt to view nature in a theological perspective derived from religious experience and historical events—which is an enterprise very different from a *natural theology* derived from reflection on nature alone. I submit that the idea of a God of persuasion is consistent not only with the contemporary understanding of nature but also with the God of love known in religious experience and in the worshiping community.

4. Is any inclusive world view possible today? One facet of secularity is its skepticism, not just about classical Christian metaphysics, but about the possibility of any unified interpretive system—even a scheme which emphasizes nature, temporality, and human freedom. Secular man, it is said, accepts provisional answers to limited questions. Here I can only say that there is in me—as I think there is in all men, especially in scientists—a drive to unity and coherence. I am convinced that beyond the fragmentation of unrelated languages there lies one world, though our understanding of it is always partial. Moreover, in any sustained thought about the world it is impossible to avoid metaphysical assumptions or general concepts with which one interprets and organizes events. If the implicit world view in terms of which one lives and acts is not theistic, it will be pantheistic or naturalistic, or express some other ultimate commitment.

Yet we can agree with secularity to this extent: our efforts at system are *tentative and partial.* We must avoid the kind of absolute claims on behalf of a completed and closed synthesis which characterized classical Christendom. We can acknowledge the inadequacy of all our models of God. We can also give greater attention to the implications of various models for the manifold functions of religious language—implications for worship, for social ethics, and for attitudes toward nature. Hopefully, then, contemporary religious thought can recognize the legitimate concerns of secularity about the tentativeness of all world views, as well as about the autonomy of nature and the freedom of man.

CHAPTER THREE

The Technological Mentality

SUPERNATURAL COTTON

And so it came to pass that nature made cotton. And it was good. But then it came to pass that man improved nature's cotton. And it was better.

It had more luster, more strength, and more richness of color. And it was called *Durene* mercerized cotton. And so, at last, man rested.

Helene Davis of *Carillon Fashions,* however, decided that instead of resting she'd make this elegant dress with double-breasted jacket. . . .

And it was very good.

Advertisement in *N.Y. Times Magazine,*
March 1, 1970

Science is not only a way of knowing and a way of viewing the world; it is also a way of doing, a way of controlling nature. Man's outlook has been transformed by *applied science and technology,* science as power rather than as knowledge. Even if belief in God is not rejected in theory in the name of the scientific method or the autonomy of nature, it may be ignored in practice because it appears irrelevant to the contemporary world. Here it is the relevance of religion, rather than its credibility, which is at issue. Here the focus is more on ethics than on philosophy or theology.

I will be looking, then, at another facet of *secularity*. The laws of nature can be understood without reference to God; but in addition the world seems to be controlled by man, not by God. It is a world of natural forces available for man's conquest, an object at his disposal. Secularity denotes not only man's intellectual autonomy and his institutional autonomy, but also his practical autonomy to guide his own destiny. Secular man is interested in this world; he has lost interest in otherworldly sanctions and goals. He sees religion as an obstacle to his freedom and fulfillment. His confidence and trust are in human capacities expressed in technological power. By his own abilities and efforts, man reached the moon. I want to analyze in this chapter the relation between secularity, the technological mentality, and biblical religion.

I. The Biblical Roots of Secularity

Let us start by recalling that many features of secularity are not only consistent with biblical religion but are supported by it. In particular, three implications of the doctrine of creation are congenial to both technology and secularity:

1. The intelligibility of nature without reference to God. Hebrew religion differed from most ancient religions in holding that the world is neither divine nor demonic. The doctrine of creation expressed the conviction that nature is orderly, dependable, and intelligible. These assumptions became part of the outlook of Western man and, according to most historians, contributed indirectly to the rise of modern science. The biblical view, far from being antithetical to secularity in this sense, has in fact helped to produce it. Nature has built-in orderly structures which can be studied by man without explicit reference to God.

2. The goodness of the material world. If nature is created by God, it is essentially good rather than evil or illusory. In the Genesis narrative it is said of every created thing: "And behold, it was very good." Judaism and early Christianity endorsed affirmative attitudes toward the world, though these were modified by later currents of other-worldliness and life-denial. The Bible itself gives a very positive evaluation of matter and time. God is served in the world, not by renouncing it or withdrawing to a separate religious sphere. The biblical view of the dignity of work perhaps also contributed to western cultural attitudes which were congenial to technology.

3. Man's dominion over the earth. If nature is not divine or sacred, man is free, in the words of Genesis, "to fill the earth and subdue it, to have dominion over the fish of the sea and over the birds of the air and over every living thing." Man was called to name the animals and to tend the garden. Psalm 8 says: "Thou hast given him dominion over the works of thy hands; thou hast put all things under his feet." Can we not think of technology as a fulfillment of the commission to subdue the earth? Only in our century has such dominion become effective —dominion over microorganisms by medical advances, dominion over space by supersonic planes and space flight, dominion over time by television communications linking the world, and so forth.

In addition to these ideas of the intelligibility and value of the world and man's dominion over it, other biblical roots of *the secularization of nature* have recently received considerable attention. Arend van Leeuwen has argued that in most nonbibilical cultures of antiquity, both nature and society were viewed as established and fixed divine orders. Kings and priests and social structures were thought to be divinely sanctioned, and nature was permeated by sacred power. But biblical religion desacralized nature, so man could study it and use it. The social order was also desacralized by the conviction that no ruler or state is absolute and no institution is beyond God's judgment. Man was liberated from all false absolutes embodied in sacrosanct social institutions.[1]

Van Leeuwen maintains that the biblical outlook also brought a new *openness to change.* History was viewed as linear and progressive, not as a recurrent cycle. Man was responsible to reshape institutions rather than to accept an immutable order from the past. Van Leeuwen asserts that *technology* is today bringing precisely this same kind of liberation to newly emerging nations, challenging the sacred order of traditional cultures, shattering their established institutions, and opening man's life to a new future unlike the past. Technology, he says, is Christ incognito, liberating man from the authority of tradition.

A similar thesis is presented by the German theologian, Friedrich Gogarten. Christian faith *frees man from bondage to the powers of the world.* It considers all institutions as limited and partial; it keeps the secular really secular, devoid of all religious power.[2] The Christian is called to be autonomous and responsible. Gogarten makes much of St. Paul's statement in Galatians that we are sons and heirs, delivered from tutelage into maturity. Recall also Dietrich Bonhoeffer's references to the maturity, autonomy, and adulthood of "a world come of age." Modern man no longer needs God as hypothesis or as helper. He does not need religion as an explanation or as a way of solving problems.[3]

We are not concerned here with the historical reasons for either the rise of technology or the secularization of the social order. Any historical judgment would surely have to take into account the contribution, not only of biblical religion, but of Greek rationalism, Renaissance humanism, and the Enlightenment's confidence in man, as well as economic and social forces in the growth of industry. Our concern is rather with the attitudes engendered by technology and its consequences in human life. Are these attitudes and consequences consistent with the values upheld by biblical religion?

II. The Social Impact of Technology

Let us ask, then, what impact technology has actually had on the quality of human life in society. We run at once into sharply divergent appraisals. At one extreme are the enthusiasts who see technology as *the great liberator of man.* New drugs, better medical attention, and improved health standards have more than doubled the average life span compared with a hundred years ago. Machines have released us from much of the backbreaking labor which in previous ages absorbed most of man's time and energy. The ancient dream of a life free from suffering, famine, disease, and poverty is beginning to be fulfilled through the applications of science. Technology seems to be the main source of hope for the Third World of newly developing nations.

Automation and *cybernation* are eliminating much of the monotonous work typical of early industrial society. The economist Robert Theobald foresees a day when only 2 per cent of the population will need to work to produce abundant food and goods for the entire nation. Such an increase in productivity could bring, not only the elimination of poverty and toil, but the enrichment of man's life and the flowering of his creativity. Through most of man's history, leisure and culture have been the privilege of the few, at the expense of the misery of the mass of humanity struggling for mere survival. Now universal abundance can free man—for continuing education, for the arts, for social service, for participation in community life and politics.[4] In Chapter Five these potentialities of cybernation and leisure are discussed in detail.

Moreover, the urban society which technology engenders brings *new opportunities for choice* which were not present in the small-town agrarian society of the past. Harvey Cox maintains that people who long nostalgically for the good old days have idealized and romanticized the past. Small-town life was actually very constricting, and a person's choices were severely limited by his family status and the community's expectations. The very impersonality and anonymity of the city now allow him the freedom to choose his friends and preserve his privacy when he wants it. Social and geographical mobility allow a greater choice of job and location; a person does not have to follow his father's profession and can establish his own self-identity. Man is liberated from static and confining traditions; he can assume mature responsibility for his own life. The enthusiasts extol these positive contributions of technology to human life.[5] This kind of optimism seems to be rather common among scientists and engineers.

At the opposite extreme are the critics who see technology not as man's liberator but as his enslaver. To them, technology is *a threat to authentic human existence.* They view it as a power which man cannot control, a system with its own momentum. It is autonomous and self-determining, leading a life of its own, following its inevitable course. Technical progress has consequences which cannot be foreseen, results which no one intended, changes so rapid that we cannot adapt to them. Like the sorcerer's apprentice—who learned the magic words to make his broom carry water but forgot the formula to make it stop —we seem to have set in motion forces which we cannot direct. We ask, "Where is science taking us?", not "Where are we taking science?"

This critique of technology has of course been prominent in the *existentialist tradition.* Kierkegaard and Dostoevski, Marcel and Tillich, Sartre and Camus, each protests in his own way against the conformity of mass society, and each defends human freedom and individuality against all forces which turn man into an object. Among recent authors, Jacques Ellul has given one of the strongest indictments of the depersonalizing and dehumanizing character of technological society.[6] He points to the regimentation, standardization, and conformity which result from mass production of goods and mass media of communication. Within a uniform technical culture, differences among individuals and among groups tend to disappear. The objectification and mechanization of interactions between deadened human beings has been vividly portrayed in the Theatre of the Absurd (e.g., Samuel Beckett, Harold Pinter).

According to these critics, *the impersonality of power* in a technical society jeopardizes individual responsibility. Persons become cogs in a well-oiled machine. Processes are segmented so that each man contributes only a limited operation, with little opportunity to participate in decisions concerning over-all goals. One's relationship to other men is compartmentalized and functional; life is fragmented into a series of limited and mechanical interactions. Man ends not the master of the machine but its servant, adapting to its schedule and its demands. If consumers do not need a new product, the desire for it is created by high-pressure advertising; with planned obsolescence, even last year's model is out of style. The "hidden persuaders" manipulate people for their own ends. When such attitudes infect the political order, it is only a step further to the "human engineering" of Huxley's *Brave New World* or Orwell's *1984*. So say the more pessimistic social critics who foresee the enslavement of man to the machine. Their view seems to be common among artists, authors, and an increasing number of our youth.

What are we to make of these divergent appraisals? Is technology man's liberator or his enslaver? The easy answer is to say that science is *ethically neutral,* and that its results are good or evil according to the way they are used. The consequences of a particular discovery will indeed depend on how it is employed; atomic fission may be used to generate electricity or to vaporize a city. But technology as a whole has a more pervasive and total impact on man's life and thought, going beyond the uses of any particular discovery. Both the optimists and the pessimists rightly recognize that we do not simply face specific ethical decisions in a familiar context; we face a new context, a radically new human environment, an emerging sociocultural system.

However, the technological patterns which emerge are not so *inevitable* as the pessimists maintain. They have seemed inevitable in the past only because adequate mechanisms of control and guidance have not been created. Technology has been an instrument of profit and power. We have assumed that the pursuit of private profit would yield social benefits, and that the "invisible hand" of the market place was an unconscious agent of automatic progress. But the actual consequences of technology have been very mixed, and part of our task is empirical research on these social effects (such as the Harvard ten-year study on Technology and Society) as a basis for social policy.[7]

The basic problem, then, is *the responsible control of technology.* This is not easily achieved because technology concentrates power, as in the alliance of science with the military-industrial complex today. Moreover, a dominant technical elite tends to develop, since only a small group of experts have the knowledge necessary to make significant decisions. Experts are often impatient with the slowness of democratic processes and the shortsightedness of the common man. The technocrats and social engineers know they could run society more efficiently. They assume that social problems are amenable to the same approach as problems in applied science; decisions will be more rational if they are made by those who are best informed.

But the purported objectivity of the expert often conceals his implicit value judgments. When computers play a role in decision-making, their conclusions seem objective and unchallengeable, but their operation may conceal the judgments of the man who wrote the computer's program. *Man's motives are ambivalent,* even when he believes he is dedicated to the best interests of society. Whenever social planners think they are wielding power for the good of all—whether in the French and Russian revolutions or the enlightened scientific elite of the future—the relative innocence of moral intentions seems to be corrupted in historical actualization.

We will thus always need *social controls over the controllers.* No man is good enough to be totally entrusted with the destiny of his fellow men. In a technological society it is crucial to preserve a plurality of centers of decision-making, and to encourage intelligent participation in choices at a variety of levels—by unions, management, political parties, state and national legislation. We need new institutions of participatory democracy in which the people most directly affected by policy decisions can have a more determinative voice in their own destiny (see Chapter Six).

III. Dangers in the Technological Mentality

We have been looking at the impact of technology on the social conditions of human life. Let us now consider the impact of *the technological mentality* upon human attitudes—a more subtle influence perhaps, but a pervasive one. The dangers here lie, not in technology as such, but in uncritical preoccupation with technological goals and methods. I will list four of these dangers.

First, *exploitation of the environment.* The technological mentality engenders a utilitarian attitude toward nature. Combined with an individualistic view of private property and the sanctity of profits, it has led to far-reaching destruction of our natural environment. Our forests have been cut and burned, our rivers polluted, much of our wildlife exterminated. Half our productive soil has been lost. Think of the ravaging of redwood forests which took centuries to grow, or the death of Lake Erie from industrial wastes. We poison the environment with noxious chemicals, fumes, sewage, detergents, pesticides, noise, and heat. We dump 200 million tons of trash annually, including 28 billion bottles and 48 billion cans. We foul the atmosphere with smog (which someone has called the Air Apparent). We release long-lasting pesticides which are starting to kill off birds and fish. American women have in their breast milk concentrations of DDT 3 to 10 times higher than the government allows in dairy milk for human consumption.

There has been considerable ecological concern recently, but it will be short-lived and ineffectual unless it deals with *the exploitative attitudes* which have led to environmental deterioration. The basic disease is man's arrogance toward nature, the predatory spirit that leads him to plunder the earth. If we treat a succession of symptoms—seeking technical remedies for one form of pollution after another—the task will be endless; unless the disease is cured, its expressions will simply take new forms. Moreover, the technical "solutions" often have unforeseen repercussions; detergents utilized to disperse oil slicks evidently harm marine life more than the oil itself. Now the exploitative attitude is in part a by-product of the Christian tradition, as Lynn White has pointed out.[8] The Genesis narrative has been taken as a justification of man's subjugation of nature. Man is portrayed over against nature, rather than as an integral part of it. One might almost conclude that in the Bible nature has no reason for existence except for man's use.

But if one-sided emphasis on the theme of "dominion" has contributed to the crisis, the recovery of other biblical themes can show us a way out. C. F. D. Moule insists that the creation story implies *responsibility and stewardship.* [9] In the Old Testament, the land belongs ultimately to God, and man is only its trustee. The Bible speaks of care and respect for nature. The created order is valued in itself, not simply as a service to man or as instrumental to human purposes. God delights in it and cares for it apart from man (Psalms 19, 89, 104, etc.). Recall how Job was finally overwhelmed by the majesty and wonder of nature. Recall St. Francis' deep love of the natural world, his sense of the dignity and equality of all creatures, his response to what he called his sister the earth—not mother earth, as in the pagan religions, and not earth as an object to be exploited, but sister earth. Consider the lilies of the field, said Jesus. God notices the sparrow's fall—even if the culprit was DDT.

We also need to acknowledge *man's interdependence with nature.* In the preceding chapter I criticized both the radical separation of nature and history in existentialism, and the neo-orthodox view of nature as a neutral stage for the drama of human redemption. I indicated the need for a theology of nature. Today we are more aware that man is part of nature, not its master and manipulator. He lives in a total ecological community, an interdependent web of life. He participates in a creative process, a complex order whose welfare he cannot ignore with impunity. He knows his kinship to the whole community of life, and his responsibility to future generations. In place of the alienation of technological man from nature, we must recover a respect for the natural world with which we are inseparably linked, a sense of wonder and reverence for life. Attitudes toward nature are fundamental in the development of an ecological conscience. Exploitation can give way to respect and responsibility.[10]

The second danger in the technological mentality is *reliance on power.* Technology is a potent instrument of man's purposes, and we too easily assume that it can deal with all problems. As one illustration I would point to our preoccupation with power in the Vietnam conflict. We have tried to use military technology to solve problems which were essentially social and political. When our policies did not succeed, we threw in more and more fire power. We dropped more explosives on North and South Vietnam (which together are smaller than New Mexico) than on all the Axis powers in all of World War II. In one brief operation, the defense of the marine base at Khe Sahn, we used more tons of bombs than on Japan in the whole war. A colonel said after a mission in the central highlands: "We had to destroy the town in order to liberate it." His comment describes the tragedy of Vietnam on a larger scale. Beyond the decimation of land, homes, and people is the destruction of village life and national culture. We have been blind to the human consequences of the power we wield.

No amount of fire power could achieve such crucial goals as the creation of a stable, popularly based government. It is clear that we backed a series of governments which did not have widespread support—first the French colonial forces which opposed national aspirations for independence, and then a succession of military dictators. Each was supported by only a small segment of the populace, each silenced dissent and imprisoned opposing leaders or excluded them from the ballot. Because we were preoccupied with military power, we did little to encourage a more representative government or to seek political and social reforms. We have consistently underestimated the power of ideas, including the ideals to which the North Vietnamese are dedicated. Economic and social efforts have been continually subordinated to military ones. I see in our Vietnam policy the same insensitivity to human experience and the same reliance on power which characterize the technological mentality.

The third danger is *the impoverishment of experience.* Exclusive dependence on the technological approach leads to a truncation of experience, a loss in man's imaginative and emotional life and the sensibilities expressed in poetry and art. In looking only to the public world, man's personal existence is neglected and his symbols lose their power to communicate. The calculating attitude of control and mastery militates against the openness and receptivity which interpersonal relationships require. Human love is always a gift which can't be controlled. The I-Thou relation requires availability, responsiveness, mutuality, and personal involvement, in contrast to the I-It pattern of manipulation and objective detachment. Calculation and control exclude grace and surrender; only in humility are reverence and awe known. The danger here is that technological attitudes, which are necessary and valuable in their own domain, will so dominate man's life that important areas of human experience will be jeopardized.

The assumption that *technical reason is omnicompetent* leads to the impoverishment of man's life. Reliance on a quantitative approach discourages interest in the nonquantifiable aspects of human experience. In Chapter One I noted that the role of creative imagination in science itself is left out of most accounts. How much more does "the myth of objectivity," when imposed on other areas of life, confine the human spirit and diminish man's subjective life. My plea here is for recovery of the wholeness of experience, for endorsement of dramatic and historical modes of apprehension, for self-awareness and openness to human experience in its many dimensions and its imaginative richness.

The problem, once more, is not technology but *preoccupation with technological goals.* To the scientist or engineer, research is an exciting challenge which can easily absorb all his time and energy. He may be oblivious to the social consequences of his inventions and totally unconcerned about the relation of knowledge to life. Every specialist is tempted to reduce reality to fit the categories of his own field, and to narrow his horizons to questions with which he can deal. Technical solutions and increased efficiency become ends in themselves, and there is neither time nor inclination to reflect on their implications for the quality of human life.

Similarly for the citizen a legitimate concern for material needs becomes a *frantic pursuit of comfort,* a total dedication to self-gratification. Our industrial society awakens false needs through the deliberate creation of new cravings. A barrage of advertising stimulates our appetites as consumers and engenders an insatiable drive toward greater and greater affluence. Man then ends as a slave to his own desires. Such an obsession with things distorts our basic values as well as our relationships to other persons. "A man's life," said Jesus, "does not consist in the abundance of his possessions." "What shall it profit a man if he gain the whole world and lose his own soul?"

In this context I think we must listen to *the protest of some of our youth* who question the prevailing pursuit of technological affluence. Their heroes are men like Herbert Marcuse and Paul Goodman who fear that a mechanized society will submerge personal identity. Many of the young value personal over impersonal life, spontaneity over control, the present over the future, the private over the public, the unique over the general. For them, the rationality of the technological spirit seems to repress man's vitality and emotional life. They are more concerned about authentic human existence than about a higher standard of living. They reject the pursuit of affluence, insisting that man is not primarily a consumer. They rebel against an educational system which discourages questioning and encourages conformity, training people to compete for success and preparing them to "get ahead" in the world. Their protest may sometimes take chaotic and self-destructive forms, but behind it there is often great sensitivity to the limitations of the technological mentality.[11]

The fourth danger is *unqualified reliance on technology.* According to many theologians, the essence of faith is not doctrinal belief but trust and confidence. What do you trust? On what do you rely? In terms of this definition, we must conclude that *faith in science* is characteristic of technological man. He is impressed by the trustworthiness and reliability of science, which becomes his ultimate loyalty. Technology is for him the source of salvation, the agent of secularized redemption; technological advance is his secularized eschatology. Infinite progress through technology replaces the religious infinite. This is *secularism,* an alternative faith which excludes faith in God. It goes far beyond *secularity* which, as we have seen, encourages pluralism and is itself metaphysically neutral.

Unqualified devotion to technology as a total way of life becomes a kind of idolatry, a celebration of man's glory alone, a conviction that all problems are solvable by technical analysis. Dominion over the earth becomes a Promethean quest for omnipotence and self-sufficiency. Where earlier generations spoke of understanding nature, ours speaks of conquering it. The exhilaration of conquest and power can go over into a kind of pride which verges on arrogance, especially when combined with nationalistic chauvinism. Man declares his total autonomy; he is master of his fate and the sovereign lord of his world, confident in his own abilities.

In contrast to this appraisal of human nature, *the biblical view of man* is more realistic. It sees that man in his self-centeredness alienates his neighbor and estranges himself from his fellow man. He follows paths which lead to towns named Auschwitz and Hiroshima. He lives at this instant under the threat of nuclear annihilation. Even in his calmer moments he is adept at rationalizing his self-interest, so that in human history every group appears more noble to its own members than to others. When he does act with good intentions, his actions often have tragic consequences. In the biblical perspective, man's fundamental problem is one of will and orientation and not simply of technical intellect.

Recent theology has, I think, tried to achieve *a balanced appraisal of man.* Under the dominance of neo-orthodoxy, Protestant thought overemphasized human sinfulness and dependence on God, and minimized man's creative potentialities. A new generation of theologians calls us to be co-workers with God, but it is also aware of the tragic dimension in human history.[12] Grace is not just an antidote for sin, but a positive agency evoking human creativity. The gospel holds out the possibility of a life of genuine relatedness, openness, and sensitivity when the power of love breaks into our encapsulated lives, when reconciliation overcomes alienation. This is the power which we see at work in the life of Christ, the man for others, and this is the pattern for the recovery of our own humanity.

The gospel also illuminates the question of *autonomy.* To secular man, autonomy means freedom from externally imposed authorities, among which he includes God and the church. But this negative conception of freedom *from* constraint is inadequate without a positive conception of freedom *to* act. The constraints on man are not all external; he may be in bondage to internal forces. To modern man seeking autonomy, the gospel says: you can be liberated from alienation and self-centeredness, you can be set free to love, set free for the life of involvement and service. It also says: God's will is not an external authority; it is your own true fulfillment, the law of your own being. This is the path to authentic freedom.

Biblical religion can also witness to *dimensions of human experience* which are not accessible to technical reason. It can uphold the dignity and value of the person against all attempts to manipulate or control him, and can defend individuality in a machine-dominated society. It can present a model of man as responsible self rather than as consumer or technician. It can cultivate and intensify human experience, richness of imagination, and awareness of the sacred. It can provide perspective for criticism of cultural values, reflection on the ends of human existence, and a vision of a society in which technological progress is subordinate to man's true well-being. What is required here is a basic shift in values from a "thing-oriented" culture to one which is "person-oriented" and, beyond that, "life-oriented." The goal is a society dedicated to the conservation and development of human and natural resources. We should judge our progress not quantitatively in terms of "standard of living," but in terms of the quality of life.[13]

In the contemporary crisis, *technology should be redirected,* not at all in the interests of otherworldly withdrawal, but precisely in the interests of the quality of man's life in this world. Ours is an acquisitive society dedicated to achievement, success, efficiency, and comfort. It promotes wasteful consumption and an insatiable desire for bigger and better gadgets. Advertising stimulates new wants, rather than efforts to fill basic unmet needs around the world. In a culture which worships growth and continued expansion, the ideal of balance and stability should be defended. In confronting the population explosion, as we shall see, our goal must be zero growth. Technological innovation must proceed more cautiously, with greater attention to environmental repercussions and social consequences, with restraint and moderation in the tempo of change. The United

States, with one-fifteenth of the world's population, accounts for over half the world's annual consumption of raw materials. One American uses up natural resources faster than a hundred citizens of India (some scientists would say five hundred is a more realistic estimate).[14] It would be simply impossible for the whole world to pollute the environment and exploit its resources at the U.S. rate. In the past, technology has increased the gap between rich and poor nations, and between rich and poor within our own nation; I will suggest later that the ideals of justice and equality demand a fundamental redirection of the technological enterprise.

Biblical faith, in sum, can offer specific correctives for each of the dangers in the technological mentality which I have outlined. Facing exploitative attitudes toward the environment, it can encourage care and respect for nature. Facing the impoverishment of experience, it can reassert the primacy of personal existence and interpersonal relationships. Facing unqualified reliance on technology, it can remind us of man's ambivalence, witness to the transforming power of love, and guide us in the redirection of technology.

IV. Conclusions: On Christian Secularity

Let me summarize my own understanding of Christian secularity and its implications for technology:

1. We are called to responsible maturity. We are sons and heirs in God's household, partners with him in the creative process and in the task of humanizing the world. We need not hesitate to affirm life in the world or to celebrate the secular. We are called to involvement, not to otherworldly renunciation. Secular existence is precisely the sphere of our religious responsibility. Only a false dichotomy sets the "secular" over against the "sacred." The gospel is not the enemy of human freedom and fulfillment; it liberates us to discover our true humanity, it frees us for creativity and service. Grace is active wherever authentic human life emerges, though every historical manifestation of grace is partial and ambiguous.

2. Our context is the servant church. Secularization does entail the autonomy of political, social, and educational institutions from ecclesiastical domination. But the church does not have to retreat to a separate spiritual sphere, cut off from what people consider the real issues of their lives. There has emerged a new vision of the servant church as a community of joint search and engagement in the world. Such a church can witness to the prophetic concern for social justice in the struggle for racial equality, urban renewal, and a more humane society. In an unjust social order, the church cannot simply act as reconciler between opposing factions; it may have to be an active protagonist on behalf of the underprivileged. Set free from preoccupation with its own institutional life, it can become a disciplined community of religious inquiry, acceptance, forgiveness, and active involvement in the midst of the secular world.

3. *Technology is a major instrument of social concern.* The pessimists who advocate a halt to scientific development and a return to the agrarian past are indulging in irresponsible romanticism. Our response to the neighbor in need has to be expressed technologically. "For I was hungry and you gave me food, . . . thirsty and you gave me drink . . . naked and you clothed me, . . . sick and you visited me (Matt. 25:35-36). Today it is not enough to feed the poor, for we have it in our hands to abolish hunger and poverty. The fight against debilitating sickness and oppressive misery is a technological and social problem, not only a question for individual charity.

4. *Our task is the humanization of the technological revolution.* We must strengthen the social institutions which shape and control technological forces. We must nourish those areas of human experience with which the technological mentality cannot deal, and cultivate human capacities which are not immediately useful, especially in the area of person-to-person relationships. Huston Smith has written: "The moral is not 'less technology,' but 'more of other things': more checks on the concentration of power in politics, more attention to personal dimensions of life within society, more confidence in glimpses of reality sponsored by objectives other than science."[15] Only then will technology serve man, and not man technology.

5. *Man is interdependent with nature.* Christian thought bears

some responsibility for a technology which ravages the environment, but it can now help man achieve a new understanding of his relationship to nature. Man is part of a larger whole; his loyalty must be to the community of life, not to mankind alone. We live in subtly balanced systems, and the effects of our actions reverberate throughout the created order. We must recover a basic respect for the value of all living things, a sense of wonder and reverence for life. Nature has not usually been included in the sphere of ethics; today we need an ethics of nature as well as a theology of nature. We will return to these questions in Chapter Six in considering specific policy goals in the redirection of technology.

CHAPTER FOUR

Biochemical Man

> A single body of natural laws operating on a single set of
> material particles completely accounts for the origin and
> properties of living organisms as well as nonliving aggre-
> gations of matter and man-made structures. Accordingly,
> man is essentially no more than a complex machine.
>
> Dean E. Wooldridge, *Mechanical Man*

The three challenges to religion discussed so far have arisen
from general and pervasive features of science: the scientific
method, the autonomy of nature, and the technological mentality. The fourth challenge, the biochemical view of man, arises
from a particular scientific field, molecular biology. The image
of man as a complex machine challenges the Christian understanding of human nature. I will first examine the new biological
knowledge and its implications for our image of man. Then
some ethical problems in the applications of this knowledge are
taken up—specifically, recent proposals to remake man by alter-
ing his genes. The order of earlier chapters will be followed,
moving from science as knowledge to science as power, looking successively at philosophical, theological, and ethical issues.

I. The Chemistry of Life

The most exciting scientific breakthrough in recent years has been the discovery of the structure and operation of *the DNA molecule*. DNA, as you know, consists of pairs of twisted strands, each strand a chain strung like beads on a thread. Each segment of the chain includes one of the four bases, which are set off in groups of three. Each group of bases carries the code for one of 22 amino acids, the fundamental building blocks from which proteins are made. A particular sequence of bases thus specifies the sequence in which the building blocks are assembled to form particular proteins. One DNA chain might assemble the amino acids into the type of protein found in muscle fibers, another might produce proteins for nerves, and so forth. In this way DNA carries the genetic information which governs the growth of all forms of life.

Of course, we have only begun to understand how DNA controls and coordinates *developmental processes*. In the growth of an embryo there must be fantastically complex regulatory systems whereby various DNA segments are turned on and off to control the production of specific proteins—resulting in the growth of the right kind of cell at the right place at the right time within the pattern of the total growing organism. A single human chromosome, a string of thousands of genes, contains on the order of 100 million bases—which is several times the number of words in a set of the *Encyclopaedia Britannica*. We know very little yet about the mechanisms by which these genetic instructions are "translated" into biological processes.

Nevertheless, most biologists believe that life is in principle *explicable in physicochemical terms*, without invoking any distinctive vital substance or life force. It appears probable that self-replicating molecules will be produced artificially from simpler substances. There seems to be no obstacle in principle to the laboratory synthesis of life. Francis Crick, the co-discoverer of the structure of DNA, writes as follows: "Thus eventually one may hope to have the whole of biology 'explained' in terms the level below it, and so on right down to the atomic level. . . . The knowledge we have already makes it highly unlikely that there is anything that cannot be explained by physics and chemistry."[1]

Let us look for a moment at Crick's statement that "everything will be explained by the ordinary laws of physics and chemistry." Let us grant the tremendous importance of the new field of molecular biology and the fantastic new vistas it opens. There is no sharp line between the living and the nonliving. We can agree with Crick in rejecting *vitalism*. The progress of science has been hindered by the idea that there is a vital agent within the organism, directing its growth and development. The postulation of gaps in the scientific account, in which some mysterious life force operates, has been an obstacle to further inquiry. We can grant all this, however, without accepting Crick's *reductionism*—that is, his belief that the laws of all other fields are in principle derivable from the laws of physics and chemistry. There are three kinds of objection which can be raised against reductionism:

1. Biological laws cannot be deduced directly from physical laws. Biology involves concepts which do not even occur in physics and chemistry. Biological concepts can indeed often be correlated with physical concepts, but the correlation is not provided by physics and chemistry alone.[2] Moreover, it is unlikely that biological laws will be explained by "the ordinary laws of physics and chemistry" in their present form, for these fields are not static and completed bodies of knowledge. In the history of science, the bridges built between two sciences have often been derived from neither of the original sciences. Classical physics had no connection with such chemical phenomena as the periodic table or the covalent bond, until quantum physics provided a fruitful bridge between the two fields. The concepts of each discipline were modified and expanded in relation to the other. In the border between biology and chemistry there are likely to arise new kinds of theory perhaps different from those of either field in its present form (this might involve the kind of "scientific revolution" discussed in Chapter One). Information theory, for example, is a new discipline which has in recent years illuminated a number of the traditional disciplines without being derived from any of them.

2. *Organisms are multilevel systems.* They have a hierarchy of levels of organization. A cell is a relatively stable unit, with considerable independence, self-regulation, and internal feedback controls; yet it is also a part of a larger whole to whose integrated behavior it contributes. Various kinds of concept are useful at various levels, and they need not exclude each other. System laws and higher-level theories may be valuable for analyzing types of event and activity which do not occur in the component parts separately.[3] For instance, the contribution of nerve impulses to the integrative pattern of an organism's behavior raises questions very different from study of the chemistry of nerve impulse transmission. Moreover, it appears that randomness at one level is independent of randomness at other levels (for example, in quantum physics, in molecular motion, in gene combination, and in populations of organisms). Hence, statistical laws at one level are not reducible to statistical laws at another level.[4]

3. *A variety of models may be useful.* I indicated earlier that a model is not a literal picture of reality. Alternative models representing different modes of analysis are not mutually exclusive. I maintained that any set of concepts is selective and abstractive rather than exhaustive. I would defend the value of distinctively biological concepts, defined by reference to higher-level phenomena exhibited by larger wholes. The great success of molecular biology must not lead us to neglect the conceptual schemes typical of physiology, population genetics, embryology, ethology, and so forth. Such fields use functional concepts and relational properties not definable in terms of chemistry alone.[5] We must avoid the temptation to think that the components are more real than the totality, or that a chemical analysis somehow excludes other kinds of analysis. A Michelangelo statue may be described chemically as calcium carbonate, but there are also other ways of describing it.

Against reductionism, then, we can cite the history of science, the multileveled organization of organisms, and the usefulness of a variety of models. We can accept a methodological recommendation—that *X* can be fruitfully *analyzed as y*—without turning it into a metaphysical pronouncement—that *"X* is *nothing but y."* Is man "nothing but a complex biochemical mechanism"? Man is indeed a biochemical mechanism, but that is not all that he is. We do not have to conclude that religion is just psychology, and psychology is really biology, which is merely a complicated form of chemistry and physics. We can acknowledge the laws of molecular biology but also point to distinctive higher-level phenomena in organisms and in man.

II. Man and Nature

Let us ask, more specifically, what modern biology has taught us about the status of man. From many areas of research comes convincing evidence of *man's unity with nature.* The message of ecology, which we noted earlier, concerning man's interdependence with the natural order, is reiterated by molecular biology and evolution. The same four bases make up the DNA of almost all living things; many of the proteins in different species are remarkably alike. The cytochrome enzyme in man is a string of 104 amino acids, of which 92 are identical in the horse, and 82 in the fish. Your genetic line goes back unbroken to the earliest organisms. You are, as it were, the thousandth cousin of an amoeba. You are kin to all creatures, sharing a common history. You are an integral part of nature, continuous with a long evolutionary process. And you are not necessarily the end of the line, for human evolution continues still.

The early Darwinists, anxious to prove that man is a product of evolution, stressed *man's affinities with animal life.* It was said that there are no essential differences between man and the higher apes. Since then, the rudiments of many human abilities have indeed been found in simpler creatures. Ravens can count, porpoises can form lasting friendships, and chimpanzees can make tools and interact in complex social relationships. But today biologists are more impressed by *man's unique capacities.* Human language is now understood to be radically different from all systems of communication among animals. Man can use abstract symbols and general concepts to refer to what is not present. His power to remember the past and anticipate the future liberates him from his immediate time and place. He can respond to ideal possibilities—to a vision of what ought to be, not just what is. In imagination and in act he can plan and create the genuinely new.[6]

The *distinctiveness of human culture* is also noted by many contemporary biologists. Cultural change is a new form of evolution very different from genetic change. The legacy of the past is now transmitted to the future not alone by genes, but by education, the written word, and social institutions. Again, the social character of selfhood has impressed many observers. Language itself consists of the socially shared meanings of a community. Man is inherently a social being, for the self is constituted by its relationships. Human culture is not something external to us, but is formative of our psychosocial existence. Then again, man's distinctive *self-awareness* can hardly be denied, even though it is difficult for the scientist to deal with. The scientific account leaves out the data of immediate consciousness. The experiencing subject is not an object for investigation, and first-person language is logically peculiar. Man alone is self-conscious; he alone asks who he is and knows that he will die.[7] His freedom to distinguish alternatives and choose among them is the ground of his sense of moral responsibility. Man as personal agent, responding in love to the needs of his neighbor, seems to transcend the biological world.

But now comes new evidence of the extent to which even these higher functions have *a physical basis*. A few grams of calcium can make the difference between a sociable child and an irritable one who flies into an uncontrollable rage at the slightest provocation. There are many dramatic instances of the influence of drugs on personality. More recently, behavior has been drastically altered by *electrical stimulation of the brain*. Dr. José Delgado at Yale places very fine wires in the brain of a monkey who is usually aggressive; when the current is turned on he is meek and submissive. A cat with a suitably placed electrode cowers in fear at the sight of a mouse. Move the electrode a few millimeters, and the cat will be excessively bold, attacking a dog several times its own size.[8] There are brain centers whose stimulation an animal finds almost irresistibly

pleasant. After a rat has learned to press a lever which momen-
tarily switches on the current to a pleasure center, he will ignore
food and drink to press the lever at the fantastic rate of 8,000
times an hour, for hours on end, until he is exhausted. Other
brain locations are associated with memory. One human pa-
tient, with an electrode implanted in connection with brain surgery, reported that every time the current was turned on he saw
in vivid detail a long forgotten childhood scene.

Now I want to ask whether these various biological findings
conflict with *the biblical view of man.* Certainly the Bible sees man
as rooted in nature, sharing the finitude and creatureliness of
all beings; he is formed from the dust of the earth, and to dust
he will return. In the biblical tradition, man is a social being
whose relatedness is his very being. Man is constituted by his
relationships; he is who he is precisely as father, husband, citizen, and member of a covenant people. The dominant image of
person-in-community emphasizes this social dimension of selfhood without losing the value of the individual. Moreover, the
biblical writers view man as a unitary being—a psychosomatic
unity, one might almost say. The self is conceived not as a
separate entity but as a unified activity of thinking, willing, feeling, and acting. It is this integral being whose whole life is of
concern to God. Man is a personal agent, a responsible self
interacting with other selves.

While later Christian thought, under the influence of Greek
dualism, sometimes imagined a disembodied soul imprisoned
in an evil body, the Bible itself looks on mind, body, and spirit
as aspects of *a personal unity.* H. W. Robinson writes: "Characteristic of the Old Testament, the idea of human nature implies
a unity, not a dualism. There is no contrast between the body
and the soul such as the terms instinctively suggest to us."
According to Oscar Cullmann, "the Jewish and Christian interpretation of creation excludes the whole Greek dualism of body
and soul."[9] There is, then, no biblical dichotomy between matter and spirit. In particular, the body is not the source of evil,
or something to be disowned, escaped, or denied. We find
instead an affirmation of the body and a positive acceptance of

the material order. Man is an integral being, an active bodily self.

We will be true to the biblical outlook, then, if we can view man today both as *a biological organism* and as *a responsible self.* Once again we must reject the fallacy of reductionism and defend the validity of two ways of talking about man. I suggest that this can be done partly by the notion of *levels of activity.* Man is a many-leveled unity, and the levels are not to be thought of as mutually exclusive. Some of these levels he shares with all matter, some he shares with all living things, some with all animal life, while some seem to be unique to man. Distinctive categories can be used to describe distinctive events occurring at higher levels, without denying their dependence on lower levels. Thus we need not be surprised that a lower-level event, such as the effect of a drug or an electrical current on molecules in the brain, will influence the complex patterns we call thought and emotion and personality.

The other suggestion is that *different ways of talking about man* are not mutually exclusive. As the linguistic philosophers continually remind us, there is a plurality of kinds of language which serve very diverse functions. The observer-language of the scientist does not exclude the actor-language of personal experience. Scientific discourse does not exhaust the subjectivity which is disclosed in self-awareness nor the mutuality of interpersonal interaction. The categories which illuminate human relationships and the decisions in individual life may not be those which help the physiologist develop laboratory hypotheses. We may have several *models of man* which are useful for diverse purposes. The biochemical model is not, as sometimes claimed, an all-purpose model. We need models of man both as biological organism and as responsible self.

III. Man-made Man

Up to this point I have been looking at the way in which modern biology has challenged traditional images of man. Let me turn now to the *ethical implications* of our new knowledge. Knowledge is power—in this case, power to control man himself. Human genes, like the genes of all organisms, consist of DNA chains. Our growing knowledge about DNA will give us power to influence future evolution, and perhaps eventually to remake man himself through genetic engineering. Four types of genetic control have been proposed:

1. *Negative eugenics* proposes only to limit the transmission of defective genes. It is paradoxical that modern medicine has actually produced at least some deterioration of the human gene pool. Individuals with genetic diseases such as diabetes, who in former ages might have died before bearing any children, are now sustained by drugs and can raise families; but as a result, the incidence of these diseases is increasing. Negative eugenics attempts to reduce the prevalence of harmful genes, especially those responsible for mongoloid children, feeble-mindedness, and other tragic congenital conditions. A first step would be a wide program of genetic counseling. When a case of amaurotic idiocy occurs, the parents should know that the chances are 1 in 4 that it will occur again in a second pregnancy, and they may decide voluntarily to adopt children rather than risk a repetition.[10] In other cases geneticists recommend either voluntary or compulsory sterilization.

2. *Positive eugenics* goes further and attempts to improve the human gene pool. For several decades, artificial insemination by a donor (A.I.D.) has been a not uncommon procedure. That is, if a husband is sterile or carries defective genes, the couple may ask a doctor to obtain sperm from an anonymous donor with excellent genes, so that the wife at least may bear her own child. The Nobel Prize geneticist, H. J. Muller, has extended this idea; he has proposed the establishment of *deep-freeze banks* containing the sperm of distinguished men, great geniuses of outstanding mental, physical, and moral traits.[11] If such a bank had been established in the past, a woman today might be able to choose Beethoven or Shakespeare or Newton as the father of her children. Muller insists that the choice must be voluntary, but he believes that the cumulative effect would be the gradual improvement of human character and intelligence. The proposal is certainly feasible scientifically; at the University of Michigan, twenty-nine women bore normal children from sperm frozen for two and one-half years.

3. *The selection of all the genes* of a future child would be a further step. The implantation of ova from one mother to another has been carried out in animals, and similar "foster pregnancy" or "preadoption" could be carried out with human mothers. Some scientists foresee the growth of test-tube babies. Perhaps in the more distant future, an identical twin could even be grown from the nucleus of a cell from one single individual. In some fascinating experiments, the nucleus of a frog egg was replaced by the nucleus of an intestinal cell from another frog, and an exact duplicate of the second frog developed.[12] It appears that every cell in your body carries all the genetic information to grow a new individual, though it is not ordinarily used. What if a thousand exact copies of a John F. Kennedy or a Martin Luther King might have been grown from, let us say, some of the cells of his little finger? In all the cases I have mentioned so far—negative eugenics, positive eugenics, and preselection of all genes—one would be trying to improve the human species by selecting the best of existing genes.

4. *Deliberate alterations in genetic structure* are foreseen by some geneticists. A desired DNA segment might be incorporated in a virus and used to replace a particular gene segment. Chemical or microsurgical techniques of genetic programming might allow man to be remade, custom-built according to any specifications. Perhaps a being two feet high would be advantageous for space travel, or a head twice normal size for greater intelligence. Jean Rostand envisages a new superman, scientifically engineered, with human nature radically transformed.[13] Some experts predict that within twenty-five years we will have enough knowledge to alter genes, while others assign such possibilities to a much more distant future. But all agree that direct genetic alteration would have much more rapid and far-reaching consequences on the future of man than any program of selecting from among existing genes.

The question I want to raise is *whether we should use such powers of genetic control* when and if we have them. I can see no serious ethical problems in negative eugenics aimed at *correcting defects*. If we can reduce the number of mentally retarded children, surely we have a duty to do so. I must disagree with those theologians who warn that to tamper at all with genes is to find fault with the Creator's work. David Townsend, for instance, tells us not to criticize perfection, for this is the best possible world.[14] Can one really say that to a mother who has just given birth to a second mongoloid child? Here I would side with Emil Brunner, who tells us not to identify man's present nature with the nature intended by God. Surely we have an obligation to improve mankind in every way we can—culturally, socially, and also genetically.

Let us look at *artificial insemination,* which makes only a small contribution to genetic improvement. The doctor selects a sperm donor of strong genetic heritage if the husband is infertile or has defective genes; the wife's genes are transmitted and she can have the experience of giving birth to her own child. Paul Ramsey argues that any type of artificial insemination is incompatible with Christian ethics.[15] The realm of *procreation,* he says, should never be separated from the realm of sex as an act of *love.* He endorses contraception as a temporary provision for love apart from procreation as long as the two realms are united in the total life span of the couple. But Ramsey holds that A.I.D., which involves procreation apart from sexual love, would sunder what God united.

I would agree on the centrality of love, but I would suggest that *procreation* must be considered in the context of *other forms of love* apart from sex—for example, love in the growing family and concern for the welfare of future generations. If we approve of the adoption of children, why not the half-adoption which occurs in A.I.D., or even foster-pregnancy through implantation, in cases where normal conception is impossible or inadvisable? All of these would be acts of love in a wider sense and would entail the continuing relationships of responsible parenthood. Surely it would be a misguided act of love for a father with a genetic defect to risk bringing a mentally retarded child into the world if A.I.D. would have ensured a healthy child.

Pope Pius XII has stated that *A.I.D. is adultery* and therefore must be condemned.[16] One might point out, however, that none of the usual grounds for condemning adultery applies in the case of A.I.D. That is to say, it does not involve sexual intercourse outside of marriage; the wife does not even know who the donor is. Moreover, there is no breach of fidelity, trust, and love; the husband has freely consented to and requested the procedure. A.I.D. does not seem to entail any violation of the marriage covenant, any more than adoption does.

I can see no inherent moral or theological objection to artificial insemination as such. However, there are *three practical objections* concerning its consequences:

1. Lack of psychological research. A number of doctors who have practiced A.I.D. for many years give enthusiastic reports of its success, citing letters of appreciation and joy from their patients.[17] The fact that all thirty-eight couples in one survey wanted a second child by A.I.D. is rather impressive evidence.[18] However, these studies were not psychologically oriented. At the opposite extreme, two studies by psychiatrists report serious emotional problems among A.I.D. parents.[19] (For example, the husband's sterility may lead to a sense of inferiority and revive the memory of childhood conflicts involving his male identity and his relationship to his mother, making it more difficult for him to accept the new child.) However, these were very small samples and were all extreme cases who had sought psychiatric help. There seem to have been no systematic studies in depth on representative samples. Adoption, by contrast, has been well studied and its particular psychological problems are better understood.

2. Lack of social acceptance. Because the A.I.D. procedure is not widely known, there is a scarcity of agencies and clinics able to provide effective counseling or screening of applicants, and the doctor may or may not have any insight into the emotional conflicts or personal problems of his patients. Again, in the absence of social approval, it will be difficult to tell the growing child about his origins; studies of adopted children indicate that attempted secrecy is usually harmful and seldom permanent. Moreover, only two states (Oklahoma and California) have laws protecting the legal status of A.I.D. children, whereas inheritance and other rights of adopted children are almost universally protected.[20] The administration of A.I.D. is entirely the doctor's responsibility, without the safeguards which surround

adoption procedures. We should perhaps campaign for social
and legal acceptance of A.I.D., but in the meantime their absence must be taken into account by any couple contemplating
this option.

3. The population explosion. The impending crisis of overpopulation (see Chapter Six) is at the moment a strong argument favoring adoption over A.I.D., since every additional child
brought into the world contributes to the current imbalance of
birth rate over death rate. However, I would conclude that *if*
effective population control is established, and *if* research has
shown no clear psychological evidence favoring adoption,
A.I.D. will in the future have an important contribution to make
to the 10 per cent of all marriages which are infertile—especially if there are fewer unwanted babies available for adoption.
With proper counseling and legal protection, the fulfillment of
the maternal instinct of many of these women should be possible in the bearing of A.I.D. children, without harmful consequences to the marriage, the family, or the social order. In
addition, A.I.D. would make a small contribution to eugenic
improvement, which adoption does not.

It seems to me that any of the proposals for genetic improvement—A.I.D., sperm banks, implantation, genetic surgery—
presents us with *a totally new problem* which no previous generation has faced, and we cannot simply follow the traditional approaches to ethics. We cannot expect to get specific advice from
the Bible concerning procedures which no one even considered
until recently, though we can take seriously the biblical conviction of the primacy of love and concern for the welfare of man.
Nor is the *"natural law"* tradition helpful; the injunction to
"follow nature" begs the central question, which is precisely
our new power to alter nature. We tamper with nature every
time a doctor administers a vaccination or a drug, or performs
a surgical operation, any of which may go far beyond the simple
"restoration of natural functioning." Man's dominion over nature now includes dominion over himself as part of nature. In
a situation of new options, the main criterion must be the contribution of an action to human fulfillment.

In other words, I don't think we should exclude any of these genetic proposals simply because it represents *a radical departure from the past.* Man does have the power to direct his own evolution, whatever he does. He is free to transform mankind in unprecedented ways. He must be open to genuinely new opportunities for the emergence of higher values. Creation is not complete. We are participants in creativity, helping to shape the future. Too often in the past the church has resisted change and failed to respond to the creative activity of God in history. But by the same token, we do not have to concede that just because a new scientific application is possible, it will inevitably occur. Applied science is not an irresistible tide; we have real choice in such questions. We are called to new freedom and responsibility, legitimate autonomy from determination by the past, and liberation from bondage to nature imagined as a static and unalterable structure.

IV. Dangers in Genetic Control

Thus I would not rule out in principle any of these proposals for genetic control. But I would go on to say that in practice I see grave problems as soon as one goes beyond genetic counseling and A.I.D. to consider social programs of eugenics. Let me mention three kinds of difficulty:

1. What is the ideal man? If we go beyond the elimination of obvious defects, for what positive qualities would we select or alter genes? Scientists often put intelligence at the top of the list; yet intelligence without wisdom or love might be disastrous. Muller hopes that sperm bank donors would be selected for intelligence plus brotherly love and moral courage. But could brotherly love be genetically fostered? To what extent are character traits directly inheritable? Would the genes of Beethoven yield new Beethoven symphonies? Somehow the children of creative geniuses are themselves seldom geniuses. The biologists have perhaps overemphasized the role of heredity, at the expense of culture and environment.

There is also a danger that present genetic choices would impose on future generations the dubious values of contemporary civilization. Of course, all decisions we make in education and social planning impose our judgments on the future. But drastic genetic proposals might result in irreversible changes; the present genetic pool would be lost forever, and some options might be permanently closed off. Does anyone really know what will be best for mankind under unforeseeable conditions a thousand years hence? Genes helpful in some environments may be detrimental in others. Also there may be unpredictable results of changes in genetic information, and unintended damage to future generations. Only in rare instances does a single gene control a single trait; most traits are the product of complex developmental sequences influenced by many genes. We have learned from ecology that tampering with subtly balanced systems which we only partially understand can have far-reaching and often unforeseen consequences. Such considerations do not rule out these proposals. But they do mean that novel procedures here have momentous implications and should be approached with great caution.

2. *Who should decide?* Should the genetic decisions be made by individual *parents*—who after all will have the major responsibility for raising children? This would allow for maximum freedom and individuality. It would encourage the diversity in the gene pool which is essential for future adaptability to new conditions. It would avoid the dangers of uniformity and the possibility that repetitive inbreeding would accentuate harmful recessive genes. The biologist Dobzhansky says he doesn't want a world with a million Galileos or a million Beethovens.[21] But are parents competent to make decisions with such far-reaching consequences? If they could choose the sex of their future offspring, a new generation might have twice as many boys as girls, or vice versa. Would parents force their own unrealized ambitions on their children through their genetic choices? The man who had always wanted to be a basketball star might try for a seven-foot son—who would probably hate basketball. Is genetic decision then a task for *a scientific elite?* But images of man are never a purely scientific question. And, as Dobzhansky asks, who will guard the guardians? I suggested

earlier that even enlightened social planners who think they are acting for the general welfare may be blind to their biases and should always be subject to democratic controls. No man is good enough or wise enough to be given unlimited power over the lives of others.

The *government* would thus have some role in genetic planning. But it is sobering to envisage the power of a dictator to raise a race of warriors or of docile slaves. Even democratically elected officials would need to be subjected to checks and balances. As Roger Shinn suggests, it would be an interesting election if we knew that the president chosen had to appoint directors of heredity in an Office of Genetic Opportunities.[22] Society will have an increasing capacity to mold our children, as it does already in our education system, but we should preserve as much local control and as much individual responsibility as possible.

3. Is experimentation justified? We still know very little about the connection of gene structure with human physiology, not to speak of character traits. The proposals for direct alteration of genes would require extensive experimentation first on animals and then on man. I'm not sure that I could justify the risk of producing abnormalities and genetic freaks. There are too many unpredictable factors, as well as perils to generations yet unborn. We simply can't experiment this way with human beings for the sake of scientific knowledge. You may have read about the doctor in Bologna, Italy, who grew human embryos for up to fifty-nine days in test tubes in his laboratory. My chief concern was not that it was "contrary to nature," as many people said, but that he was taking such a chance of producing deformed or abnormal babies. I'll always be haunted by the Nazi experiments, such as the following report on the effects of oxygen deprivation at 40,000 feet:

The third experiment . . . was conducted on a 37-year old in good general condition. After 4 minutes the experimental subject began to perspire and wiggle his head, after 5 minutes cramps occurred, between 6 and 10 minutes breathing increased in speed and the experimental subject became unconscious; from 11 to 30 minutes breathing slowed down to three breaths per minute, finally stopping altogether. . . . After breathing stopped, the electrocardiogram was continuously written until the action of the heart had come to a complete standstill.[23]

Of course, experiments on embryos are a long way from experiments on adults; nevertheless, it seems to me that if we respect the dignity of the individual we have to be *cautious about any experimentation on man*. It worries me to find Dr. Crick writing: "Take the suggestion of making a child whose head is twice as big as normal. There is going to be no agreement between Christians and any humanists who lack their particular prejudice about the sanctity of the individual, and who simply want to try it scientifically."[24] Yes, if one believes in the sanctity of the individual one cannot simply "try it scientifically," or treat a person purely as an object of experimentation. There is a certain presumptuousness and arrogance in manipulating the lives of others. Biotechnology, as a prescription for salvation, ends by making unjustified claims for itself. These are the dangers of the technological mentality to which I referred in the previous chapter. We could lose all sense of humility and limitation as well as respect for the dignity of man.

In the light of these three kinds of difficulty—concerning criteria for genetic choice, political procedures for making genetic decisions, and risks in experimentation—my own conclusion is that for several decades to come we should be *very cautious about any program of positive eugenics*. We can expand existing programs of negative eugenics and A.I.D. With our present basic genetic endowment there are so many potentialities which we have only begun to fulfill for a more truly human life. Our next steps should be in psychosocial and cultural evolution. I believe that the biotechnicians have oversold the prospects of changing human character by genetic means. Perhaps if we concentrate on the improvement of man within his present potentialities, we will have sufficient wisdom to make responsible choices later, if genetic knowledge ever does advance to the point where genes could be modified without grave risks to human integrity. We can also concentrate on developing social structures which offer greater protection against the abuses of

political power. In the meantime, I would give a high priority
to molecular biology among fields of scientific research. I would
also endorse Leroy Augenstein's suggestion that a small fraction of the funds in every research program should be allocated
to the study of its potential consequences for society.[25]

V.   Conclusions: On the Control of Man

Let me summarize what I have been trying to say. I pointed out
first that new biological knowledge has vividly demonstrated
man's unity with nature and the biochemical basis of all aspects
of his life. The DNA structure of human genes contains all the
information needed to specify a human being. It assembles the
proteins and other molecules of which a baby is composed, and
it directs the various processes of growth and development.
Then again, electrical stimulation of the brain can alter and
control the behavior patterns of animals and presumably of
men. I asserted that man is indeed a biochemical mechanism,
but not just a biochemical mechanism; he is also a responsible
self. I suggested several criticisms of reductionism, and proposed that analysis of activity at one level need not exclude
analysis at another level. One can, moreover, employ two models of man—as a biochemical organism and as a responsible self
—without considering them mutually exclusive.

The new biological knowledge will also yield increasing
power to control man and his future. Genetic control presents
new problems which have never arisen in previous history and
new options never before contemplated. We cannot simply rely
on ethical advice given under different circumstances in the
past. Nor can we be guided by a static view of what is "natural"
since whatever we do will, in effect, change nature. We must be
prepared to embark with courage and imagination on new
paths if they will contribute to man's fulfillment. On the other
hand, radical openness to the future does not mean that simply
because a new technological application is possible, it will inevitably be made. I do not share Dr. Delgado's fatalism concerning
the use of electrical stimulation of the brain to control human
behavior. He writes: "It would be irrelevant to discuss whether

physical control of the mind should be accepted or rejected, since history proves that when technology has been available it has been used and developed regardless of possible dangers or moral issues."[26]

I do not believe that we are bound, either by a past beyond which we cannot move, or by a future which we cannot escape. New applications of biotechnology need not be rejected simply because they are radical departures from accustomed patterns, nor need they be accepted as inevitable applications of our new knowledge. We are genuinely free to weigh alternative courses of action and to act on the basis of our decisions. Perhaps if man were just a biochemical machine, he could do nothing to decide his own future. But if man is indeed a responsible self, he faces momentous choices which he alone can make.

CHAPTER FIVE

The Cybernetic Revolution

Many great scientists had worked for many years building a giant computer, and had spent many months feeding data to it. Finally they were ready to ask it a question. Into the machine they typed: "Is there a God?"

The computer whirred and typed its answer: "There is now."

The fifth challenge comes from a new scientific field of which few people had even heard a decade ago. Like molecular biology, cybernetics presents a double challenge, first in its implications for our image of man, and then in the ethical issues arising from its applications. Once again, we must consider science both as knowledge and as power.

Cybernetics may be defined as *control* under the guidance of *information*. (The word was coined by Norbert Wiener from the Greek word for helmsman). Theories of control and communication were brought together in the design of self-regulating control systems. One of the key principles is the "feedback" of information which automatically regulates the operation of a system. A simple example: a household thermostat sends to the furnace the "information" that the room temperature has fallen; by closing a switch, it turns on the furnace, which heats the room—until the thermostat signals that the pre-set temperature has been attained, and the furnace is turned off again. A more complex cybernetic mechanism is the "automatic pilot" which keeps an airplane on a programmed course in a dense fog despite variations in wind and weather. In both rocket launchings and lunar landings, radar information is processed by computers which control the vehicle's operation automatically.

The concept of *information* is a very broad one. "Information theory" initially dealt with the transmission of data (e.g., the channel capacity of a communication medium), but increasingly it has asked also about the ways information is used. Here is a new way of thinking as well as doing, a new intellectual technique of wide applicability. Here is a new concern for the manipulation of symbols rather than things, an extension of man's brain as earlier machines were extensions of his muscles. In computers, electrical circuits are used to store and process information, ranging from IBM-card bank records to complex mathematical computations and computer-language programs. I wish to look particularly at the possibilities and limitations of "artificial intelligence" and the future of "electronic brains" which seem to threaten the status of man.

In later sections I will discuss *automation*, in which machine-controlled operations replace human control in industrial processes. In an automatic oil refinery, for instance, all the pumps and valves are controlled by the feedback of information from various parts of the system. Some implications of automation for work, leisure, and education will be noted. Another approach to information comes from *systems analysis*, the study of the interrelated parts of complex wholes. The systems analyst tries to deal with the many interacting components of an organized totality—an urban transportation pattern, a communications network, a military defense project, or an economic system. Among the issues to be examined below are the uses of computers in political elections and in policy decisions.

I. Computers and Brains

The psalmist asked: "What is man, that thou art mindful of him?" In the future, will we answer: "A little lower than the computer"? The idea that *artificial intelligence* might overtake men threatens our self-image. If man thinks of himself as a machine, he treats his fellows like one. As in the case of molecular biology, the traditional view of human nature is challenged by the reductionistic image of man as a complex machine. But there is also the fear that an "electronic brain" will develop "a mind of its own," and literally become man's master rather than his servant. The ascendancy of robots has been a favorite science fiction theme. In Stanley Kubrick's film, *2001: A Space Odyssey,* the computer, Hal, controls the operations of the space ship. Hal decides that the men on board are a hindrance to the mission, and as mutual distrust builds up, it tries to kill the human passengers. The last man survives only by destroying the computer's memory banks.

Can we separate science fiction from sober forecast? Computers have already displayed amazing achievements. They can carry out in a few seconds a complex series of calculations which would take a platoon of men a decade to perform. A checker-playing computer consistently beats the world's checkers champion. An architect can draw a floor plan with a light-pen on a fluorescent screen; the screen is hooked to a computer which converts his rough sketch into a visual display with exact lines and with all dimensions and areas calculated. Some enthusiasts extrapolate from these past successes and predict that computers will eventually surpass man in all fields of thought.

But the history of computer development suggests a more cautious assessment. After dramatic early successes, a number of subsequent problems proved much more difficult than had been anticipated. Here are three examples:

   1. Chess programs. At any point in a game of *checkers,* a computer can list every possible move, every possible response by the opponent to each of these moves, every possible counter-move, etc., for ten moves ahead. After applying a few rules for eliminating certain kinds of move, the computer can run through all the alternatives by trial-and-error search and select that which is best according to specified criteria. In *chess* this cannot be done; the number of possible configurations of the pieces, even four moves ahead, becomes astronomical. The best chess programs were for years beaten by amateurs. A more recent program on M.I.T.'s Project MAC wins four out of five games with amateurs, but it is defeated by tournament players; it takes fifteen minutes to run through 25,000 alternatives and select the best move. Now a human player clearly does not run through thousands of alternatives. Instead he uses clues from all over the board to "zero in" on a particular piece or situation which had been on the fringes of his consciousness. He directs his attention successively to a few promising configurations.[1]

2. *Language translation.* Despite expenditures of $3 million a year for a decade on computer programs to translate foreign scientific articles, no acceptable translations have been achieved. How does a person know which of a dozen dictionary translations of a word is appropriate? Take the two sentences, "The *pen* is in the box," and "The box is in the *pen*"; how do you know that the first *pen* is a writing instrument, while the second is a playpen? Sometimes the choice of meanings derives from a context of many sentences or paragraphs. There is an inevitable circularity, since the meaning of a word is not only determined by but contributes to the meaning of the sentence. Sometimes clues are drawn from an area of one's past experience (e.g., the relative sizes of pens and boxes in the example above). But the range of possibly relevant clues is unspecifiable and cannot be exhaustively listed. The clues may come from nonformal, extralinguistic areas of experience of which one is not aware, an unarticulated background on the fringes of consciousness. In poetry, of course, words have deliberate ambiguities, multiple meanings, and an open-ended range of associations.[2]

3. *Pattern recognition.* Electronic reading machines can identify special numbers on bank checks, or letters printed in a particular type, but they cannot read all type fonts, much less handwriting. Recognition by a human reader again involves

context and extralinguistic experience. Thus two identical handwritten letters might be read in one case as an *"n"* and the other as an *"r,"* depending on the context. (You would read a sentence as "Ca*n* you drive the ca*r*," and not vice versa, even though the first and last words were written identically.) A person, moreover, can recognize differences without being able to specify any criteria; traits crucial to recognition are not explicitly enumerated but remain in marginal awareness. One recognizes a square without counting sides; one recognizes a face, despite variations in angle and expression, without knowing how.[3]

A computer, by contrast, can identify a pattern only by matching it against a template or running through a fixed list of properties. Since the identifying characteristics must be specified, it cannot make novel discriminations of features for which it was not explicitly programmed. Marvin Minsky describes an impressive program for recognizing analogies among geometrical figures. It scores at the 10th-grade-level on the kind of high school test in which you are shown a series of figures (figure A might be a triangle outside a small square, for example), and then you are asked: "A is to B as C is to which figure (D, E, F, or G)?" The computer runs through lists of properties (number of sides, number of corners, sizes of angles, etc.) and relations (outside of, larger than, to the left of, etc.) and then selects the best match.[4] This method is surely not the way the human brain works, and it is incapable of dealing with a novel relation which is not on the list of relations with which it has been programmed. Similar difficulties attend the mechanical recognition of auditory patterns of speech.

Each of these three problems—chess, translation, and pattern recognition—has proved unexpectedly recalcitrant. But my main point is that where progress has been made with computer programs in such cases it has involved *methods quite different from human thought.* A computer receives information as discrete units, and processes it serially in well-defined sequences of steps according to formal rules. The human brain is evidently able to receive information which is global and continuous is character, and processes it without specifiable rules, partly by drawing from both the context and the indeterminate background of fringe awareness. If brains and computers process information in such different ways, there is less ground for confidence that machines will be able to do everything that man can do.

For purposes of comparison, we can think of a computer as an *analogue model* of the brain (in the terminology of Chapter One). That is, its electronic circuits are a physical construction in a different medium which *simulates* certain kinds of output from the brain. (I will suggest later that computer programs also often employ "mathematical models" of the situation being studied, e.g., an economic system.) The computer itself does not duplicate the structure of the brain, but simulates particular kinds of mental behavior by quite dissimilar operations. A computer can rival or outperform the human brain in a particular limited *function*, such as playing checkers; but since it does so in a very different way, we would not expect it to rival all the capabilities of the brain.[5]

The *ability to adapt* is one criterion for distinguishing *real* from *apparent intelligence.* Social insects, for example, carry out sequences of acts which seem to be intelligent. The Sphex wasp, when she is about to lay her eggs, stings a cricket just enough to paralyze but not kill it. She drags the cricket to the entrance of her burrow and leaves it there while she goes in to inspect things. Then she returns and drags it in, to serve as a source of food when the eggs later hatch into grubs. This looks quite intelligent, but it is actually an instinctual routine which is completely inflexible. If, while she is making her "inspection trip," you move the cricket an inch away from the entrance, she will drag it back to the entrance, leave it there, and make another "inspection trip" into the burrow. If you move it again, she will repeat those three steps again, as many as 40 times in a row, and never drag the cricket directly into the burrow; she follows a sequence by blind rote, unable to remember that she has carried out part of the routine 39 times already. She is unable to adapt to changes or interruptions, for she is following a rigid instinctual pattern which is presumably programmed in the

DNA molecules of her genes. Her real intelligence, as measured by adaptability to new situations, is, like that of a computer, rather low.[6]

Man, of course, is capable of a very wide *variety of types of mental activity.* Man operates without explicit rules and is able to respond to new situations; he is versatile and creative in confronting novelty. He can adapt to new kinds of information and deal with problems outside any established framework or anticipated routines. A computer may be unpredictable (e.g., if it contains a randomizer), but it has very limited adaptability, originality—or artistic creativity. Music and poetry composed by computers have not been impressive, perhaps in part because of the subtlety of tonal relationship and poetic metaphor, the effects of which on the listener seem to defy formal specification. Human thought is thus a multidimensioned continuum, including a large, varied, and open-ended repertoire of activities.

Moreover, human mentality is the product of a *cumulative cognitive development* which is closely linked to human needs and experiences. In the maturation pattern of a child's growth, thought is inseparable from emotion and feeling. There is a multiplicity of human motives springing from psychological and physiological needs, from man's body and his social interactions. Since the computer's activities do not develop in this manner, we would not expect them to resemble man's very closely. As Ulrich Neisser says: "The very concept of 'artificial intelligence' suggests the rationalist's assumption that man's intelligence is a faculty independent of the rest of human life; happily it is not."[7] Human perception, for instance, is a skill learned with the help of bodily movements in space. We do not start from a set of formalized rules; we start as organisms which move around and discover what these motions accomplish. Nor do we receive bare uninterpreted data; we pick out details and organize perceptions in terms of wholes related to our anticipations. In Chapter One we said that scientific data are theory-laden; here we can say that everyday perceptions are structured according to human goals and interests. Computers, by contrast, start from formal rules and atomistic data.

There is, finally, the question of *consciousness* in man. I cannot enter here the historic debate on the status of mind and its relationship to body. I can only acknowledge awareness as a feature of my own experience and ask whether I could conceivably attribute anything like it to a computer. I would submit that each of us assumes that other people feel as we do because we get responses which are appropriate in terms of our own feelings. The categories of intentionality and purpose are not inferences which we draw from a rigorously behavioral description, nor are they conclusions reached at the end of an argument. Rather we interpret bodily movements as purposeful actions right from the start (as I pointed out in Chapter Two in discussing the philosophical analysis of the language of agent and action). We find our interpretation confirmed if it allows us to make sense of a variety of patterns of activity. Similarly, we would conclude that machines have feelings if they responded somewhat as we do under a variety of circumstances. We ascribe degrees of conscious awareness to animals to the extent that their responses resemble our own, and we would do the same with machines. On this basis, one would have little ground for ascribing feeling or awareness to present-day computers.[8] This is not surprising, since the most advanced computer today has fewer circuit elements than the brain of an ant.

I do not believe, however, that we can set any definite limits on the potentialities of future computers which may incorporate radically new principles. There are already computers which, in a very limited way, *learn by experience.* A chess program can readjust the weight given to various criteria of decision (value of pieces, defensive position, possibilities in offense, etc.) and avoid repeating its mistakes. In other programs, interconnections have adjustable probabilities of functioning, so that successful patterns persist but new patterns are occasionally tried. Such a self-improving machine can modify its own program in the light of its past performance; in effect, it alters its own wiring. Its future activity is not predictable in detail by its designer. Perhaps in the future a machine could use higher-order abstractions to write its own program. Marvin Minsky states that "no program today can work any genuinely important changes in its own basic structure." But he believes we will cross a threshold in computer capabilities when they are capable of genuine self-improvement.[9]

It may be that *computers of an entirely different sort* will be constructed. Current machines are almost all digital (with two-state, on-or-off components). Perhaps devices with continuously variable components (e.g., graded potentials in ion solutions) will be developed, or ones using biological materials. We can also expect that new knowledge of the mechanisms of the brain will suggest principles useful in computer design. Physiological and biochemical research will probably reveal some features of the brain which can be duplicated in other media, and other characteristics which depend on distinctive properties of neural nets or protein molecules. We can anticipate that communication theory and systems research, which deal with "higher-level" integrated activities of networks and organized wholes, will make important contributions also. I do not see that one can assign any inherent limits to the capabilities of computers (especially with "wet" or organic components), or that one can exclude in principle the presence of some kind of awareness or feeling when high enough levels of organization of the right kind are reached. We simply don't know enough to say, and therefore we can only speculate.

If such higher-order computers could move around, they would be called *robots* or, if sufficiently man-like, *androids.* How could one tell a very complex simulation from real intelligence and awareness? Only, I suggest, by the same clues which would lead us to ascribe the latter characteristics to an animal, to another person—or to intelligent forms of life on another planet (whose outward appearance might be very different from ours). The clues would be versatility, adaptability, spontaneity, and the kinds of response which lead us to attribute feeling, emotion, purpose, and will. Like the wasp, present computers only simulate intelligence, and according to the foregoing criteria they have little real intelligence or awareness; however, this does not preclude the evolution of either wasp or computer to higher levels.

To many people, the very idea of such androids—even in

speculating about a distant future which we cannot at all foresee —seems *a threat to the dignity of man.* But I wonder whether this reaction is justified. Our belief in human dignity rests, surely, not on claims of the uniqueness of man, but on the value of certain qualities of selfhood (love, freedom, intelligence, creativity) which would be significant *wherever* they occur—in man, in androids, or in life on other planets. If an android had feelings and could participate in interpersonal relationships, we would need two models of such an android, as we now need two models of man: as a mechanism and as a responsible self (though as an android self rather than a human self, since there might be both parallels and significant differences). To be sure, there would be major ethical problems, both in what we did to androids and in what they did to each other and to us. This would be a crucial new stage in man's power over the future. Decisions about educating androids might be even more far-reaching than our present decisions about educating our children. Decisions about the design of androids might be more momentous and more fraught with dangers than decisions about the genetic control of man-made man. But in terms of our image of man, I would hope that if, in some distant future or on some distant planet, we find that *responsible selfhood* is not limited to human beings, we will not value it any less, in ourselves or in other beings.

II. Automation and Leisure

We must return from these rather fanciful speculations about the future to some practical problems closer to home. Let us look at some of the ethical problems arising from applications of cybernetics, starting with those in industry. *Automation* is the automatic control of any industrial process. An automated machine has a programmed operation and a feedback of information concerning its performance which enable it to control itself with a minimum of human supervision. Where 1,000 radios were once assembled daily by a crew of 200, one man now runs a complex machine with the same output. A solitary individual in the control center of an oil refinery presides over acres of equipment. In some cases, computers can provide the entire control for machines (the combination has sometimes been called "cybernation"). As industrial machinery replaced man's muscles, so automation is now replacing man's mind in repetitive or rule-governed procedures.[10]

Many routine jobs have thus been eliminated. One immediate effect, of course, is *technological unemployment* and the need to retrain displaced workers for new kinds of job. Automation has not yet resulted in the mass unemployment which some economists had expected. Robert Theobald's prediction that 2 per cent of the population will be able to produce abundance for the whole nation seems a distant goal.[11] Nevertheless, automation is dramatically increasing the productivity of each worker, and it will undoubtedly shorten still further the average work week. The six-hour day and the four-day week will soon be here.

Automation thus creates new patterns of work and leisure for which traditional ethical norms are simply inadequate. Luther and Calvin spoke of the relevance of Christian faith for *a person's job,* saying that any useful occupation could be a service to God and man. They emphasized individual virtues on the job, such as honesty, thrift, and hard work. In their day, a man could make his own ethical decisions in the course of his work, and could make a significant product by his own labor. But today it is the machine and the total organization which is productive, not the individual. Most of the important decisions about work are made by men in groups, not as individuals. Responsibility in such a situation requires not individualistic virtues but awareness of the social implications of one's work and intelligent participation at the points of industry and government where decisions are made (see Chapter Six).

The prospect of *widespread leisure* also presents a challenge which man has never faced before. In an earlier day when there was so much to be done, leisure was viewed as a time to recuperate for work. Under frontier conditions, idleness jeopardized group survival. In the Puritan ethic of hard work, the idle were looked on as sinful. In part, this judgment represented a reaction against the luxury and display of an older aristocracy. But these attitudes, which are evident in restrictive Sabbath laws, undoubtedly hindered creativity in leisure and in artistic imagination.[12]

An age of automation requires *a new philosophy of leisure,* considered not just as a respite from work but as an opportunity for service, growth, and enjoyment. Most Americans are unprepared to use leisure creatively. With shorter hours required on the job, they often work overtime or take a second job, preferring an increased income rather than increased leisure. Free time frequently leads only to boredom, or to new ways of "killing time." (In the average American home, the TV set is on for almost seven hours a day as it is.) Let me list, then, three components of a philosophy of leisure:

First, leisure can provide *new opportunities for voluntary service.* In social work, in teaching, in hospitals and community agencies there will be endless scope for imaginative contributions to human need. Participation in political and civic life could be vastly expanded. The preservation of the environment could provide many activities for an ecologically conscious generation. Peace corps and technical assistance projects will be needed for decades in underdeveloped countries before hunger and misery are wiped out. Concern for the establishment of social justice and racial equality can surely find myriad expressions through churches, unions, political parties, and action groups. We are called not simply to aid the victims of exploitation but to change the exploitative structures of society.

Second, leisure is *an opportunity for self-fulfillment.* In the past, work has been a central source of personal identity; in the future, many people will have to find their sense of meaning and purpose largely in so-called spare time activities. Leisure is an important means of self-discovery in which new awareness of one's potentialities is found. The cultivation of arts and crafts increases sensitivity to one's environment and to one's own human capacities. Here also is engendered the respect for individuality which can easily be lost in a mass culture. Literature and drama are doors to understanding and insight as well as to enjoyment and personal enrichment. Genuine fulfillment includes the experience of significant human relationships, which increased leisure could encourage. Again, meditation and contemplation, which are crowded out by our pragmatic culture, might find a larger place if self-discovery were seen as a goal of leisure.[13]

Third, leisure is *an opportunity for play*. It is an expression of the whole person, as against any intellectualization of existence. It is a celebration of the meaningfulness of life. Here we could take our cue from the Jewish Sabbath which despite its restrictions is a day of joy and affirmation. Perhaps we have something to learn also from Eastern religions concerning appreciation of unity with nature rather than mastery over it even in our outdoor recreation. We could rediscover a new form of justification by grace rather than duty, a liberation from compulsive work. Leisure can be *re-creation* and genuine enjoyment. It can also be an expression of social unity in celebration together, and a bond which unites the family in common activities.[14]

Now these new patterns of work and leisure have significant *implications for education*. When technological change is rapid, many skills have to be taught on the job and revised as the technology changes. General methods of approach will be needed, rather than memory of information; facts can always be obtained later by mechanical information-retrieval devices. Education for leisure will increase in importance as education for a job declines. Here too the encouragement of creative originality will replace memory and repetition. A broad liberal education could develop critical appreciation and individual expression in the humanities and social sciences, so that people will be participants and not spectators in the arts and in social change. Education will be seen as a lifelong process, encouraged by continuing adult study as well as informal self-education.[15]

It seems likely, in fact, that *the line between work and leisure* will become increasingly blurred. It is common to find enjoyment of the job for its own sake among professional people—scientists, painters, musicians, professors. Conversely, spare-time do-it-yourself projects or voluntary work are often similar to paid jobs. If in the future a small fraction of the populace can indeed produce abundant goods for all, some sort of guaranteed annual income will be necessary to sustain purchasing power and to provide a minimum standard of living. The link between job and income would be broken, and the distinction between paid and unpaid work would have vanished. Each person would have the basic conditions both for a decent human existence and for work which he considered significant. With purchasing power guaranteed, the artificial stimulation of needs by advertising, which occurs in an economy of scarcity, would diminish. These further ramifications of an automated society and an economy of abundance may not be fully possible for a number of years, but it is not too early to begin to plan for them.

III.   Systems Analysis and Policy Decisions

In addition to industry, other areas in which computers have been applied include politics and government. As a first example, imagine a candidate for the U. S. Senate who hires a public relations firm to construct *a computer model of his electoral constituency*. Into the computer are fed data from previous elections and polls and special surveys; it predicts the reaction of the electorate to a variety of issues and personalities. The candidate's image is then molded in such a way as to maximize the vote; he is told what positions to take and which issues to avoid. Just as the Madison Avenue behavioral scientists can use market research on consumer preference to manipulate acceptance of a new product, so the new political advisers can simulate voting behavior and provide a blueprint for winning an election. The optimum image will be specified by the computer.[16]

Such *molding of a candidate's image* to fit data on voting behavior has been increasingly prominent in recent elections. Nixon's campaign strategists gave particular attention to his national TV image, and several state contests were virtually run by public relations firms. But the use of computers to simulate an electorate and to merchandise the optimum candidate seems to undercut the democratic process of debate and the elucidation of issues. The emergence of genuinely new and imaginative ideas is hindered since the computer is tied to extrapolation from the data of the past. We may need to have legislation limiting polls in advance of elections, like the laws which prevent polling a jury in advance of their decision in court. Perhaps when the pollster knocks on my door I should tell him that the voting booth is the proper place for expressing my political choice.

As another example, consider the proposed *National Data Center*. Here in one giant federal computer would be stored all the information now scattered in various files. There would be a complete dossier on every citizen: tax records, police entries, bank accounts, credit ratings, draft classifications, job applications, medical histories, social welfare records, school grades, FBI data, and so forth. Such a centralized data bank would be of great value to the Internal Revenue Service in tracing tax evasions, to local police in convicting criminals, to government agencies in predicting trends, and to social scientists in correlating a multitude of variables. But the potential abuses and invasions of privacy should give us pause. Who would have access to confidential information that could destroy an individual's career? What protection would be afforded against errors in reporting or recording? When a computerized magazine subscription goes astray, or you get billed for someone else's purchases or phone calls, the mistake is not serious; but mistakes in your national dossier might wreck your life. It would be essential that everyone transferring information into or out of the data center be identified and recorded, and access would have to be strictly limited. For research purposes the computer could be programmed to yield only statistical data and no data on individuals.[17]

I want to examine in greater detail the use of computers in *policy decisions*. The new field of "systems analysis" takes an interdisciplinary approach to total interacting systems such as urban transportation networks or missile defense schemes. Like the ecologist, the systems analyst is aware of the interrelatedness and mutual dependence of the parts in a total whole. "Operations research" involves the coordination and organization of control systems, e.g., design of an airport traffic guidance and landing plan. "Game theory" is used to assess strategy in conflict situations. Instead of moving pins on maps, today's generals fight wars on computers which simulate the effects of nuclear attacks and predict the number of Russians and Americans killed under various combinations of circumstances.

Systems analysis can be very helpful in showing *the probable effects of alternative courses of action.* It can aid policy decisions by presenting the costs and consequences of changes in the system, on the basis of a specified set of assumptions. Computers can of course make such calculations very rapidly. Radar information on the pattern of missiles in an enemy attack can be analyzed and retaliatory strike plans formulated almost instantly. (The computer could be programmed to decide on the optimum plan and launch retaliatory missiles automatically, but at present the final decision at least is made by men.) There have been several recent applications of systems analysis to urban problems. Simon Ramo's *Cure for Chaos* argues that analytic methods developed in aerospace research can be applied widely to social technology.

There have been more ambitious proposals for the use of computers for the *rational ordering of society.* The effects of social changes could be predicted, and the actual results could be continuously monitored and the information fed back so that policies could be corrected and adjusted. The whole operation would be planned by a technical elite, a professional managerial class (of which we have the forerunners in the aerospace and military-industrial complex). The concentration of decision-making power and the centralization of rationalized planning would be carried a stage further. Like the classical utopians, the new social planners are often impatient with human imperfections; they claim that only a technical elite can understand the complexities of systems analysis and the rational decisions which are called for.[18]

I will return later to the problem of the power of a technical elite. At the moment I want to suggest three limitations in the use of computers in policy decisions:

1. Models are not pictures of reality. The systems analyst usually constructs a mathematical model to represent formal relationships among selected variables. Models of quantitative features of social systems are of course particularly amenable to computer programming. A simulation of the carrying capacity of an urban transportation system or a cost/benefit analysis of an industrial innovation can be readily accomplished by constructing suitable mathematical models. But, as Norman Faramelli writes: "The analyst must remember not to take his model too seriously. The model is not an accurate representation of reality; it is a tool used to help him better understand the interrelationships between numberous variables."[19]

As we saw in Chapter One, models are based on *simplifying assumptions* which are often of limited validity. Game theory assumes "rational behavior" on the part of its participants. Some economic models assume "free competition" which is rarely even approximated in modern industry. Max Weber's "ideal types" in social theory are not descriptive of actual societies. Often the key assumptions reflected in a model are not recognized. The story is told that, at the height of the conflict, a Defense Department computer was asked when the Vietnam war would end; it replied: "According to my calculations, the war ended six months ago." Moreover, the systems analyst is often so fascinated by the technical problems of model building and computer programming that the limitations of his calculations are ignored.

2. *Social decisions involve many variables.* Computers can deal most easily with one-dimensional problems, such as cost/benefit analyses using purely economic terms. But social problems are multidimensional, and many of the significant factors are qualitative rather than quantitative. The nonquantitative factors tend to be relegated to a footnote and omitted from the computer program.[20] Systems analysts have difficulty coping with ambiguous or nonlogical aspects of society or human nature. Yet the value of a computer result depends entirely on the data and the assumptions fed into it. The president of a firm which had just computerized its inventory control system commented: "We get the same wrong answers, only now we get them faster." Computer people have a principle known as GIGO (Garbage In, Garbage Out).

Once again, *omitted factors* may be the most crucial ones. In urban planning, it is easier to predict the effect of a freeway on tax rates than its effects on racial tensions or the disruption of a neighborhood. In predictions of survival following nuclear attack, property damage and medical injury can be quantified, but the psychological impact of social disorganization is usually ignored. Herman Kahn in *On Nuclear Warfare* claims that strategy calculations must take into account not only high priority objectives but also those of medium and even low priority. But in practice his computer is programmed for victory in nuclear war, rather than for the prevention of war. He thus endorses civil defense measures which would minimize losses even though they might be seen by Russia as a provocative act and thereby increase the chance that war would occur.

3. Value judgments influence computer programs. A computer print-out appears objective and infallible, and some systems analysts claim that it provides a scientific basis for social planning free from all value judgments. Others hold that the computer itself can present the consequences of alternatives objectively, so that values enter only later in the decisions made by social planners after the work of the computer is done. Still others see value judgments entering at the start when the programmer makes assumptions, limits the alternatives, and establishes criteria. I would argue that value judgments enter throughout and are usually unrecognized. In an earlier chapter I suggested that scientific paradigms influence the data obtained; in the social sciences also, different paradigms yield different perceptions of reality. The constraints defining the context, the variables considered significant, and the criteria of evaluation are all value-laden. The goal of "optimizing the system" usually conceals these assumptions.

For whom will a proposed change be beneficial, and who will bear the indirect costs? There are usually *conflicting value centers* involved in any social decision. When special interests or biases go unnoticed, politically selected options are legitimated as if they were purely technical conclusions. In a computer analysis of pollution control in Delaware Bay, the programmers' objectives favored goals typical of middle-class recreation, such as boating and fishing, rather than those of the urban poor, such as swimming. In computer programs for matching job openings against persons seeking jobs, many of the descriptive categories used were inapplicable to the underprivileged, and intelligence was measured by formal education.[21] A computer is used in Vietnam to select targets for American bombers. It weighs probabilities and cost/efficiency ratios based on intelligence data of varying reliability concerning enemy activity of varying extent (a trail or river crossing known to be used occasionally, a forest area rumored to contain hidden supplies, a village reputed to shelter collaborators, etc.). The number of innocent farmers or villagers who might be killed is not an important consideration; the program simply assumes that American lives are dear and Vietnamese lives are cheap.[22]

We seem to have two rather distinct groups on the American scene: persons expert at *technical analysis* and persons motivated by profound *social concern*. The computer experts seldom question their own value assumptions or fundamental goals. On the other hand, the radical social critics, including most of the New Left, show considerable moral sensitivity and concern for the victims of social exploitation, but almost total disdain for the detailed knowledge and technical competence required if their ideals are to be realized in practice. There are all too few individuals who combine technical ability and moral sensitivity.

IV. Conclusions: On Men and Machines

Cybernetics is an instrument of man's purposes and an extension of his capacities. As the industrial revolution relieved him of routine mechanical work and augmented his physical power, so the cybernetic revolution relieves him of routine mental work and *augments his intellectual power*. The man working on the assembly line was mechanized, conforming to the demands of the machine; but the man programming a computer controls its action and communicates with it on his own terms (through a visual-display screen, for instance). Cybernetics employs a new set of intellectual tools, chief among which is the concept of information. New techniques for transmitting, storing, processing, and using information are employed; new forms of symbolic representation and the manipulation of symbols are introduced. I have particularly noted the ways of thinking characteristic of systems analysis (and also characteristic of ecology): an interdisciplinary approach, a concern for total systems, and a recognition of interdependence. Systems analysis can make an important contribution to social planning; it can help man understand the consequences of alternative actions and can encourage him to examine his assumptions and goals.

The *practical benefits* of cybernetics are manifold. Computers have already been a boon to almost every branch of industry, government, and education. As a means of data storage, computers can replace mountains of paper and years of time in processing the records of banks, companies, universities, state and federal offices. If you travel by plane, you are indebted to computers for the plane's design, the airline reservation, the air traffic control system, and probably the pilot's paycheck. Defense missiles, space launchings, and lunar landings are all controlled by radar-and-computer systems. Before long, computers will undoubtedly be used for medical diagnosis and for legislative and legal reference. Perhaps in a future election or a national referendum you will vote from your home by dialing coded telephone digits which feed into computers. Perhaps whole libraries will be instantly available anywhere by summoning a page of any book to your television screen or photo-copying machine.

Cybernetics, then, is an instrument of *man's purposes.* But those purposes are not themselves derivable from computer programs. The ends to which technology should be directed are matters of human choice. The biblical tradition would insist that cybernetics must serve human welfare. The prophetic concern for social justice and equality would remind us of the needs of the underprivileged over against the space and military demands and industrial profits which have governed much of the development of computer applications. Programmers control machines, introducing their own value judgments and basic assumptions; but ultimately the electorate must control the programmers when crucial decisions are at stake. Computers enhance the power of the technical elite who know how to use them; the control of the controllers can be accomplished only through the political process. These questions of policy and procedure in the redirection of technology are the subject of the final chapter.

CHAPTER SIX

The Redirection of Technology

In the past, we have had science for intellectual pleasure,
and science for the control of nature. We have had science
for war. But today, the whole human experiment may hang
on the question of how fast we now press the development
of science for survival.

John Platt[1]

Planet earth faces a series of crises involving technology. The
four most imminent threats of global catastrophe are nuclear
war, the population explosion, poverty and hunger in the Third
World, and environmental deterioration in the industrial West.
These impending calamities reflect a deeper problem: a crisis
in values. They also reflect a social problem: our inability to use
political institutions to control technology effectively. The last
challenge presented by modern science—and it will also be the
last for mankind if we do not respond to it creatively—is the
redirection of technology. In the late sixties, 90 per cent of
federal funds for research and development went to defense,
space, and atomic energy; a reassessment of national priorities
in applied science is imperative.

I. Man in Space

As a case study in values and policies in the uses of technology, let me start by examining the U.S. space program.[2] The most dramatic technological achievement in history was the landing of man on the moon. It was indeed a fantastic demonstration of what can be accomplished by a large-scale technological effort directed toward a single goal. It was a triumph of *teamwork and cooperation,* a coordinated mobilization of men and machines. It was a victory for human imagination, ingenuity, and organization. We can have nothing but admiration for the intelligence of the scientists, the skill of the engineers, the competence of industry, and the courage of the astronauts, which together made possible this feat of corporate man.

Why did the moon landing evoke our enthusiasm? In part, because it was *a challenging and exciting adventure* into totally new realms. The astronauts encountered experiences never previously known to man: the strange weightlessness of space, the amazing sight of our own planet earth, the stark beauty of the desolate moon. These men gave us new hope and a sense of human creativity and dignity. Frustrated in our search for peace and prosperity on earth, we welcomed the success of achievement in space. The story became a twentieth-century epic, with its heroes and martyrs, its rituals and cultic celebrations. In a wider sense, the astronauts are a symbol of freedom from bondage to the past and of openness to the radically new potentialities of the future, a symbol of the power and secular initiative of technological man. In the blast-off of those gigantic rockets we experienced man's power, his autonomy and mastery; it represented a new extension of his dominion over nature.

But there were in the space venture other motives which seem more dubious, motives that reflect the ambivalent nature of man to which the biblical tradition points. Consider the role played by *national prestige.* The initial commitment to land on the moon in the sixties was a political decision made by President Kennedy in 1961 against the recommendation of his scientific advisers. It was announced, shortly after the Bay of Pigs fiasco and the first Russian orbital flight, partly as a means to restore the nation's prestige.[3] Eight years later the astronauts fulfilled the Senate resolution calling for the U.S. flag alone, without the U.N. flag, to be planted on the moon (as if the scientific laws we used came from that all-American team of Galileo, Newton, Einstein, and von Braun). No, the whole program was in part an expression of nationalism and rivalry. Space spectaculars were geared as much to public relations as to scientific or social benefits. Let's face it: our chief concern was the space race, not the human race.

The space venture was also motivated by *national pride*. (Pride, I take it, refers to one's own self-esteem, whereas prestige refers to the esteem in which one is held by others.) Our culture is oriented to competitiveness, achievement, success. The launching of Sputnik was a great blow to our pride; we experienced it as a national humiliation. Congressional debate resounded with assertions that we cannot run second, we must be the world leader, we must regain first place. But the question is: in what do we take pride? Is technological skill dominant in our self-image? Why not pride in clearing slums, or in eliminating starvation around the world? Pride and humiliation are expressions of what we value most. Why are we humiliated by another country's achievements in space technology, rather than in education or decent housing, social justice or racial equality?

Military defense was of course an additional consideration. The Air Force, which was fighting for its existence, emphasized possible military uses such as orbiting nuclear bombs; but most observers have held that space weapons would be vulnerable, difficult to guide, and of dubious military value. Yet many congressmen felt that, even in the absence of clear military missions, space capabilities should be developed as a contingency insurance against unforeseen possibilities which might catch us by surprise. The space effort has aided missile technology and strengthened the interlocking aerospace industry. But note that these indirect military applications (such as reconnaissance "eye-in-the-sky" satellites) have come from unmanned near-space programs. There never was any military purpose in manned orbital flights, much less lunar ones. No one has proposed a plausible military use for the moon.

Space expenditures were also thought of as *a stimulant to the economy.* They were defended as a response to unemployment. But space industries require highly skilled personnel, and are located in relatively prosperous parts of the country; they have been of no real help to the unemployed. There was supposed to be a large "spin-off" to civilian industries, but defense and space research have little relevance for consumer goods. A few companies have been heavily subsidized, but the transfer to the broader economy has been small compared to the investment. There have been occasional industrial uses (e.g., temperature-resistant materials developed for re-entry nose cones can be used for furnace linings), but such direct applications are rare. Out of 1,200 prime research contracts and thousands of subcontracts, there were only 23 patent applications.

The evaluation of a policy decision, however, requires careful assessment of consequences as well as motives. There are, of course, some *practical benefits,* though these have come almost entirely from the near-space unmanned program. Since the flights themselves were more a feat of engineering than of basic science, they have contributed mainly to technological developments, especially in metallurgy, electronics, and cybernetics. There have been indirect economic benefits, such as the Telestar satellites used for television communication and the Tiros satellites used for weather forecasting. There will also be important *scientific gains.* Greater knowledge about the moon will help us understand the whole solar system, and will give us a better picture of the early history of the earth before its erosion by wind and water. But it is clear that most of the scientific benefits could have been achieved at far lower cost by unmanned vehicles. Manned flights cost roughly ten times as much as unmanned flights. And man is a very limited scientific instrument; he must use other instruments to record and gather data which can only be analyzed back on earth.

Few scientists would claim that the scientific benefits could justify *the enormous costs.* The Apollo program alone, up to the first landing, cost $24 billion. In a typical year, NASA's budget was $5.1 billion, including $700 million for basic research, while the National Science Foundation (the agency for basic research in *all* the sciences) received $300 million.[4] A poll of a random sample of members of the American Association for the Advancement of Science found that only 1 in 20 favored a space program of this magnitude. Even the Space Science Board (of the National Academy of Sciences), which is composed mainly of space enthusiasts, has favored unmanned rather than manned moon landings. The NASA program has been very costly in personnel as well as in funds; it has diverted scarce talent away from other fields. Philip Abelson, editor of the AAAS journal, *Science,* wrote: "I believe the diversion of talent to the space program is having and will have direct and indirect damaging effects on almost every area of science, technology and medicine."[5]

Alvin Weinberg, director of the Oak Ridge National Laboratory, has proposed *a set of criteria for priorities* in the allocation of funds among *scientific fields.* Some of these criteria are internal to science: the ripeness of a field for development, its relevance to other scientific disciplines, the competence of the scientists involved in it. Other criteria are external to science: its potential contribution to technology and to human welfare. Weinberg gave top marks to molecular biology on all these criteria; it could contribute immensely to many other sciences and, through medicine, to human welfare. To the development of nuclear energy he gave low marks on scientific contribution but high marks on relevance to human welfare. But to space exploration he gave a low rating on both scientific and social criteria.[6]

But what about the future? The President's Space Task Group has recommended a program aiming at *a manned Mars landing* in the 1980's. (This group, composed of the Vice-President, the Director of NASA, the Secretary of the Air Force, and the President's Science Adviser, was hardly a neutral panel; all its members were on record already as favoring this conclusion.) The price tag on the Mars landing, including intermediate goals such as orbiting space stations and reusable reentry vehicles, is about $100 billion.[7] In contrast, the Space Science Board of the National Academy of Sciences, in a series of reports from 1961 to 1969, recommended relatively inexpensive *unmanned flights*—to Mars and the nearer planets until 1975, and to the outer planets from 1975 to 1980. The House Subcommittee on Space Science, chaired by Congressman Joseph Karth, urged the expansion of unmanned earth satellite programs, and sharply criticized NASA for neglecting them in favor of manned flights.[8] A number of top NASA scientists have resigned in protest over the neglect of scientific objectives in Apollo planning.

Space research also presents an unparalleled opportunity for *international cooperation*, rather than rivalry. Eugene Rabinowitch, editor of the *Bulletin of the Atomic Scientists*, proposes that we offer Russia participation in Apollo missions in exchange for U.S. participation in Soviet flights.[9] Such cooperation would avoid wasteful duplication and would save billions of dollars; it might conceivably help to break the vicious circle of mutual distrust and pride. Until we have tried to make space research international, there is more rhetoric than reality in the words of the plaque our astronauts left on the moon: "We came in peace for all mankind." Why, incidentally, might there not have been at least a black face among the various all-American astronaut teams?

Some of the other arguments used to support *manned flights to Mars,* as distinct from unmanned flights, seem to me rather dubious. Take, for instance, the argument by analogy: "Why did men climb Mt. Everest? Because it was there." Yes, but a daring adventure by a few individuals is one thing; a major national commitment that takes human and material resources away from more urgent needs is quite a different matter. Or again, the analogy with Columbus is misleading; there is no realistic prospect of bringing back economic riches from space or opening up vast new areas for human settlement. Even the top of Mt. Everest is hospitable compared to the moon's desolate vacuum and extremes of temperature. Mars seems almost as forbidding and the round-trip will take two years, while travel to the nearest star will take many lifetimes.

It has been suggested that we should *transfer human colonies* to Mars in order to ensure the survival of our species in case a nuclear holocaust wipes out man on earth. Wouldn't it be better to spend the same time and energy preventing such a tragedy —unless we totally despair of man, in which case we can have little confidence that he will fare any better on another planet? Further, I do not agree with those who say that when a technological application is possible, it will inevitably occur. Technology is not a monster that goes its own way, or an autonomous force which, once set in motion, we cannot control. On the contrary, the decision is up to us.

The allocation of funds, I suggest, is basically *a question of priorities.* With $100 billion we could land a man on Mars. Or with $100 billion we could go a long way toward transforming our cities and changing the pattern of poverty in our nation, and still have enough left for unmanned flights which would bring most (though not all) of the benefits to be gained from manned flights. If we are looking for challenge and excitement and the sense of an open future with genuinely new possibilities, could we not find these in the conquest of hunger, disease, poverty, and war? The moon program has shown what can be accomplished when resources and determination are coordinated toward a single goal. The question now facing us is: For what purposes will we use these impressive technological capabilities? Are we so preoccupied with national prestige or technological achievement for its own sake that we will buy space spectaculars at the expense of human misery?

If we look beyond our own nation, it is clear that *the growing gap between rich and poor countries* is largely the result of technology. A billion people live in relatively prosperous countries with more than $600 per capita annual income (Gross National Product divided by population). At the opposite extreme, two billion live in impoverished countries with less than $150 average income. Between the two extremes there is only a handful of countries, totaling less than a hundred million people, with average incomes between $150 and $600. The per capita income in the U.S. is $3,500, almost thirty times the average figure ($120) among developing countries. Moreover, the U.S. level rises $150 a year, while that in developing countries rises only $6 a year; thus the gap is continually increasing. Two-thirds of mankind never gets a square meal, while one-third is overfed. An American dog has a better diet than most children in India. If we recognize that frustration of expectations produces chaos and violence, our own self-interest, as well as our concern for human welfare, should prompt our action. But our affluence has muffled the cries of human need.

This tragic inequality among nations can be decreased only by a concerted *world development program.* The United Nations has called for developed countries to allocate 1 per cent of their Gross National Product to world development; several church groups have urged the allocation of at least 2 per cent (including both government and private sources). During the Marshall Plan, U.S. assistance was 2 per cent of the GNP, and the figure was 1 per cent as recently as 1961, but it had fallen to 0.3 per cent by 1968 and a meager 0.22 per cent in 1970. Expenditures for defense are roughly forty times foreign aid appropriations; those for space, roughly twice the foreign aid outlay. An allocation of 2 per cent ($19 billion) for world development would be a modest goal compared with the annual increase of 6 per cent in our GNP, or with the 9 per cent which goes to defense. In order to foster a significant growth rate in the emerging nations, we must join other developed countries in a major new program; in addition to low-interest loans and private investment, the interest received from previous loans could be reassigned to world development.

Such development funds should be channeled *multilaterally* through the U.N. and regional programs, and it should involve genuine partnership in planning and administration. Freer trade agreements and more liberal tariff policies would encourage economic growth which in the long run would benefit all nations. We should also mobilize U.S. agricultural technology to help other countries to improve their food production. We can share our knowledge and skills through an internationally directed technical assistance program. New strains of grain and the use of fertilizer, irrigation, and farm machinery could significantly increase yields per acre. The cost of the Vietnam war would have provided for substantial modernization of agricultural methods in *all* of the developing nations.

The world now possesses the technical capacity to *lift the burden of poverty and hunger* around the world. The imaginative use of science and technology for such goals would enlist the enthusiasm of university faculty and students everywhere. The Peace Corps has given us a glimpse of how our discontented youth might, through an international peace corps, rally to such a challenge. Here, surely, is a goal for technology more urgent than landing men on Mars. That picture of our spinning globe, as seen from the moon, reminds us that we're all together on this small planet. Let us commit ourselves to making it habitable for man. The biggest challenge of all, as Norman Cousins says, is to prove that intelligent life can exist—on earth. If we meet that challenge, there will be plenty of time left to go to Mars.

II.   The Population Explosion

But poverty and hunger will inevitably increase unless the *growth of the world's population* is stopped. Since the dawn of man, it took until 1850 to produce a population of one billion people. To reach two billion took 75 years more (until 1925). The third billion required only another 35 years (1960). The fourth billion will have taken 20 years (1980), and the fifth, 10 years (1990). At the current rate, the present population of 3½ billion will have doubled shortly after the turn of the century. It is ironic that medical advances can lead to human misery. In many countries the birth rate has increased slightly while the death rate has been cut in half. Each day 324,000 babies are born on our globe, but only 133,000 persons die; so there are 191,000 more persons to feed every twenty-four hours. Each week the equivalent of the city of Cleveland is added to the world's population. Each year the increase is more than the entire population of France, Belgium, and Holland. In the next decade, India must face a net addition of 150 million persons if current growth continues.[10] This is a problem of utmost urgency; the longer we wait, the more difficult it will be to achieve effective control.

The rate of population increase is highest in *the underdeveloped countries,* which can least afford it. In Costa Rica or the Philippines, for example, the population now doubles in 20 years; in Egypt or Kenya the doubling time is 23 years. In order to keep even their present meager living standards, such countries would have to double their food production and double the number of doctors, teachers, schools, and factories in a couple of decades. Hard-won gains in agriculture and industry are being more than wiped out by the increase in the number of mouths to feed. In many countries, children under the age of sixteen constitute one-half the population (as compared to one-quarter in countries with stable populations); the proportionately smaller adult fraction has a tremendous burden in feeding and educating the huge numbers of youth—who will soon become the parents of a yet-larger baby boom. Overcrowding, unemployment, malnutrition, and the frustration of expectations will lead to continuing misery, unrest, food riots, and civil chaos unless drastic action is undertaken before it is too late. New high-yield grains and intensive farming methods can increase food production, but will not even keep up with a population in which hunger, malnutrition, and starvation are already prevalent. Per capita food production in Latin America is actually less now than it was in 1935. These countries have to run faster and faster just to stay where they are.[11] Moreover, intensive use of fertilizers and pesticides are likely to have dangerous ecological effects; agricultural development is not a long-run solution to exponentially increasing populations.

Nor can overpopulation be ignored in *the United States,* since it contributes to urban blight and environmental pollution. We have 6 per cent of the world's people, but we use over half of all the raw materials consumed. It would be simply impossible for the whole world to maintain the present U.S. rate of consumption of resources. Each American baby will in its lifetime directly or indirectly use 26 million gallons of water, 21,000 gallons of gasoline, and 10,000 pounds of meat. With 200 million persons already, we will exceed 300 million by the end of the century at present rates. The quality of life is bound to deteriorate if current trends are extrapolated (increases in urban congestion, juvenile delinquency, school overcrowding, ecological devastation, etc.). There has been a lot of interest in pollution recently, but very little concern for the population density which is one of its causes. Furthermore, we cannot urge population control on other countries unless we practice it ourselves, lest it seem like a weapon of the affluent white world and an evasion of our responsibility for peoples we have exploited in the past.[12]

Proposals for dealing with the population crisis can be grouped under three headings according to the degree of coercion involved:

1. Compulsory medical measures. Paul Ehrlich holds that even the most effective crash program cannot now prevent the starvation of hundreds of millions during the 1970's. William and Paul Paddock predict widespread famine by 1975. According to these men, the unequal equation of births and deaths will be balanced mainly by a rise in the death rate, but the magnitude of the catastrophe can be diminished by the adoption of drastic measures to cut the birth rate in half. They argue that bearing children can no longer be regarded as an inalienable right if it leads to large-scale human tragedy and suffering; in a crisis situation, social policy has priority over individual choice. These authors want the U. S. to withhold food aid from countries which do not take stringent action to achieve zero population growth.[13]

In India a program was proposed for compulsory sterilization of every man after his third child, but it raised such a storm of protest in parliament that it was dropped. Several authors have recommended that a temporary sterilant be placed in water supplies (however, it is dubious that such a method could be safely used or that it would be practical in rural areas). Perhaps a lifelong contraceptive shot or time capsule could be given to every girl at the age of ten; the antidote which would neutralize it would be strictly controlled by the government. Permits for childbearing have been proposed—with a limit of two per couple if a stable population is to be maintained. Kenneth Boulding has advocated the issuing of two salable licenses to every young woman, which would allow the rich, who can afford to raise larger families, to buy licenses from the poor; the market value would adjust itself according to the over-all desire for children. Other authors have urged compulsory abortion to terminate illegitimate pregancies. These proposals all involve strict governmental control of the birth rate.[14]

2. *Economic and social pressures.* Financial incentives and penalties could strongly favor small families but leave the actual decision to each couple. Whereas present income tax deductions favor large families, deductions could be limited to the first two children. There could be taxes on births after the third or fourth child, or bonuses to a couple for each three years of childless marriage. There is some question as to how effective such incentives would be (bonuses offered in European countries during the 1930's to achieve the opposite goal, population expansion, seem to have had little effect). In addition, such measures would severely penalize the children of irresponsible parents and trap them in the cycle of poverty. A more effective method which would preserve some choice would be the offer of bonuses to those willing to be sterilized. The government could pay the cost of all abortions; in Japan, the decline in birth rate of 50 per cent between 1948 and 1960 is partially attributable to legalized free abortion, along with strong government support of family limitation.[15]

Other authors have stressed changes in social structure which would influence family size. Birth rates are lowered by any forces postponing marriage: increase in the minimum legal age for marriage (as occurred in India), availability of education and careers for young women (as in the West), changes in marriage mores, etc. Kingsley Davis has advocated a redefinition of the role of women, including participation in more jobs apart from motherhood and child-rearing, with expanded employment opportunities outside the home. He recommends an alteration of our social system and a radical de-emphasis on the family resulting from the development of substitutes for family interests as the center of a woman's life. Again, couples in many societies want large families in order to have sons to support them in their old age; this motive would be obviated by a social security system of old age insurance. All of these proposals would attempt to influence behavior by noncoercive rewards and punishments or social changes.[16]

3. *Voluntary contraception plus intensive education.* The family planning approach allows maximum freedom for the individual, and hence demands less readjustment of prevalent attitudes. It can be linked to programs of maternal health and child care. Bernard Berelson, after a detailed comparison of alternative proposals, urges the extension of existing family planning programs which already have considerable momentum and are widely accepted. Voluntary contraception prevents fear of pregnancy and the problem of the unwanted child, but it also effects considerable reduction in the birth rate. The poor in the U. S. want to limit their family size (to less than three children, according to one study). The obstacle to their use of family planning is not lack of motivation as much as institutional failures, such as the inaccessibility of medical services except in emergencies, and the grossly unequal distribution of medical care among various income groups. In Louisiana the birth rate among low-income families fell 32 per cent, and the illegitimacy rate 40 per cent, in the three years following the introduction of birth control services in the state's clinics in 1965.[17]

In Taiwan the use of intra-uterine devices (IUD loops) has been moderately successful. It is true that the decline in national birth rate started before the IUD program was under way and is attributable in part to economic development and urbanization. But a dramatic impact was evident in Taichung, a large city in which the project was first launched. Though critics point out that the service was used most heavily by mothers who already had several children, half the users were in the 25-34 year span and the birth rate was significantly lowered. Evidence from India is more ambiguous and indicates that major educational efforts are needed to reach younger mothers and to change traditional attitudes. But Roger Revelle of the Harvard Center for Population Studies states: "There is evidence that significant numbers of village women and their husbands strongly desire not to have more children, and are eager to use effective birth control methods."[18]

To cut birth rates sufficiently, a voluntary program must not only prevent unwanted births but must also encourage parents *to want smaller families*. It must convince people of the seriousness of the crisis (many college girls have recently resolved not to have more than two children). It must promote the image of small rather than large families, e.g., on television serials. The life-style of the small family must be legitimized, and the cultural symbols of family success altered. Small transistorized TV sets could bring the message even to rural villages in India. An intensive educational effort is called for not only to disseminate birth control information but to persuade people to seek smaller families or to adopt if more than two children are wanted.

Between these three types of program, no simple judgment is possible. We cannot rely on an ethic from the past, since overpopulation is a new and urgent problem never faced before in human history. "Be fruitful and multiply" (Gen. 1:28) may have been sound advice to ancient Israel, but not to modern India. An innovative ethic based on human fulfillment must be open to new alternatives. *Cost, effectiveness,* and *administrative feasibility* are certainly relevant criteria in weighing these proposals. Sterilization after two children would be the most effective of the currently available methods. It would be moderately costly (especially in use of medical or paramedical personnel) and would impose a considerable administrative burden on a developing country; but in the long run the cost would be more than paid for by the reduction in the number of mouths to feed. Bonuses would be costly and probably not very effective.

On the other hand, *family planning* coupled with intensive *education* holds out considerable promise of effectiveness at relatively low cost. To reduce the birth rate significantly, a large-scale worldwide birth control program with massive funding, administered through the United Nations, would be required. This might entail a large core of field workers, neighborhood and village clinics, and educational television transmissions from orbiting satellites (one of their more promising nonmilitary applications). To reach younger women, a greater use of the schools for education in family planning would be essential. There should be a much larger allocation of funds for research, especially on inexpensive long-lasting contraceptive pills, and on means for controlling the future sex of a child (so that each family could be assured of a son). There is also need for extensive social research, both on cultural obstacles to family planning and on attitudes toward family size. A variety of approaches should be tried, with careful study of their effects. Such programs could incorporate some of the proposals from the second group above, e.g., efforts to provide a larger role for women outside the home, a better social security system for old age, etc.

Another factor in the weighing of alternatives is the balance of *freedom* and *coercion*. In a crisis when its survival is at stake, a society may have to qualify individual freedom. Garrett Hardin recognizes that taxes and bonuses are a restriction of freedom, but he holds that "mutual coercion, mutually agreed on" is necessary to avert tragedy. "The only way we can preserve and nurture other and more precious freedoms is by relinquishing the freedom to breed, and that very soon."[19] In an interdependent society, the freedom of one man—and another, and another—may eventually imperil every man's survival; even the most basic "rights" may have to be reevaluated under new conditions. Freedom *from* constraints is empty unless it brings freedom *for* a creative life. I will suggest below that we must shift our emphasis from individual to social values. The urgency of the global crisis seems to demand coercive measures.

Nevertheless, *some forms of coercion* may be so repressive that they jeopardize human dignity. Compulsory measures which were strongly opposed by a populace could be enforced and evasions could be detected only by a regulatory bureaucracy that verged on police state methods, endangering hard-won freedoms in other areas of life. Because of the risks in the manipulation of human lives, the maximization of freedom is an important goal, even at the price of some loss of effectiveness.

I am inclined to think that the social and economic pressures advocated by the second group above combine coercion and freedom in a balance which is justifiable in the light of the current crisis. Taxes and incentives seem to me acceptable forms of coercion which we use for many social goals. (Perhaps the use of bonuses for small families, adjusted in inverse proportion to family income, would avoid imposing undue hardships on the children of poor but irresponsible parents.) Finally, from a practical standpoint, we should concentrate on policies which have a reasonable chance of acceptance by nations around the world; this would rule out most of the drastic forms of compulsion in the first list above.

Thus I would favor a vastly expanded family planning program and education for smaller families, coupled with attention to social factors contributing to birth rate reduction. Economic incentives should be tried in experimental projects. Abortion laws should be repealed, but contraception is clearly preferable, by all of our criteria, as a method of population limitation. Research in new contraceptive methods and assistance in family planning and education at home and abroad should be one of our highest national priorities—immediately. The time is now. Since you started reading this chapter, ten thousand babies have been born.

III. The Control of Technology

Let me devote a final section to the broader question of the planning of technology. Among the reasons why technological development must be a question of *national policy* are the following:

First, *the poor have benefited least from technology.* Unemployment from automation hits the unskilled hardest. A freeway is seldom used by the ghetto residents whose houses are torn down to make room for it. Supersonic planes, built with a government subsidy of $5 billion, will mainly benefit the skilled workers in aerospace industries and the affluent who can afford to fly. Both within our nation and between nations, technology tends to increase the gap between the rich and the poor. Inequalities in our society are self-perpetuating. The disadvantaged are of course most powerless and most vulnerable to exploitation. Moreover, technology seems to have a basically conservative impact insofar as it reinforces existing power structures. For example, autos are no longer a viable solution for the urban transportation crisis, yet they are perpetuated by powerful lobbies from auto and highway industries, insurance, oil and gas companies, trucking unions, etc., which block public transit schemes and other alternative solutions. Only political pressures representing the public welfare can be effective against the pressures of special economic interests.

Second, *the "invisible hand" of the market place is inadequate to control technology.* Classical *laissez-faire* economics assumed that if each person sought his own profits the laws of supply and demand would regulate economic production and yield the social good. In the past, resources were bountiful, detrimental social effects were tolerable, and private enterprise in the U. S. did engender productivity and higher standards of living— though not without considerable government regulation, and not without great inequalities in the distribution of its benefits. Technology in particular became a major instrument of profit and power. The financial rewards often went to the person who could find new ways to exploit our natural resources cheaply, to make a quick return on his investment. Today the social cost of that exploitation is intolerably high, and new forms of tax, fine, and incentive are needed so that the person who really contributes to the general welfare is rewarded. The influence of technological decisions is now so pervasive that it cannot be left to the vagaries of the market place. Choices involving automation, transportation, and communication affect us all and must be made collectively. The future is our corporate responsibility as we act through our political institutions.

Third, *the social costs of technological innovations must be paid by their users.* Insofar as possible the price of an item should reflect its total social cost and not simply the immediate cost of production. The cost of resource conservation, pollution control, and waste disposal should be carried by the producer and hence ultimately by the consumer. If soft drink manufacturers were assessed for the disposal of empty cans, they would try to minimize the total cost (production and disposal) and not just the cost of production. The users of autos should pay the public costs of the air pollution they create. New methods of "social accounting" have been developed which allow at least some estimate of such costs, though technological innovations often have additional consequences which are not evident for several years. In an interdependent society, the effects of technological decisions are drastic and far-reaching, and must be controlled by social and political as well as economic means.[20]

National planning and control should go beyond the prevention of harmful consequences and foster *the positive development of technology* in socially desirable directions. Technology is the greatest single influence on the future, and it is indeed subject to social control; it appears as an inevitable and autonomous force only because adequate mechanisms for its guidance have not been created. The growth of particular technologies has been determined more by technical feasibility and economic profit than by social need. The political system has been unable to structure the issues presented for public debate so that the popular will can be expressed concerning these momentous decisions.

In the planning of science, as much freedom as possible should be maintained in *basic research* as distinct from applied technology. In "pure science" the dominant motive is intellectual curiosity, the pursuit of knowledge for its own sake apart from any applications. Moreover, the consequences of fundamental discoveries are seldom foreseeable. In basic research there is considerable self-regulation provided by the internal structure of the scientific community. A scientist's work can be understood and appreciated only by his peers. Selection from among the applications for government grants (e.g., under the National Science Foundation) is made entirely by panels of scientists. Although some decisions have to be made concerning the allocation of funds to various fields, we should allow the scientific community and the universities, in which most of our fundamental research is done, to have maximum freedom in the management of pure science.

In the past, it has been assumed that basic science would

ultimately contribute to human welfare, and *applications in technology* would be beneficial to man. We have had an implicit faith in automatic progress, understood in terms of productivity and higher living standards. We have thought, as Don Price indicates, that "scientific knowledge, like economic initiative, could be relied on to produce progress if government could be persuaded not to interfere."[21] The scientist has been confident that if he was dedicated to the pursuit of truth alone—science as knowledge rather than as power—he would both directly and indirectly serve humanity. But these assumptions have increasingly come into question. There is a new sense of personal moral responsibility among scientists, similar to that felt by the atomic scientists after World War II, but now evident among researchers in many fields. This concern is seen in refusal to work on defense projects and in increased activity in informing the public concerning the social consequences of science.[22] Valuable as is such individual moral responsibility among scientists, however, it cannot be viewed as the main means for controlling the applications of science.

For decisions about applied science are basically questions of *national policy.* Annual federal funds for science add up to more than $17 billion, of which some 90 per cent goes to applied fields. The alternative to government guidance of technology is domination by giant corporations or military interests, since applied science is such an expensive proposition. Deliberate technological innovation on a large scale is a new phenomenon in history. Space and defense projects have shown what can be done when there is a concerted mobilization of resources for national goals. Only nationwide planning can take into account the disruptive impact of technological change, the repercussions throughout an interdependent society, and the long-range interests of future generations. Decisions must be made by the public if the general welfare is to be protected from the destructive consequences of new technologies, and if innovation is to be channeled into areas of greatest social benefit.

We have never had *a coherent national science policy.* Instead we have had a mixture of *laissez-faire* with crash programs in response to a succession of crises, from Sputnik to pollution. In the absence of clear long-range goals, we improvise with *ad hoc* projects and piecemeal solutions whose consequences have not been analyzed. We have abstract ideals and short-run programs, but few long-run policies to bridge the gap between. Budget decisions are determined largely by pressures from the vested interests of special agencies. NASA and the Defense Department, for example, have large public relations forces which promote their own projects and solicit congressional support; they have far larger staff resources for advancing their own causes than either Congress or the White House has to watch over them.

Our fear of "government interference" in applied science is in part the product of *an individualistic concept of freedom.* But in an ecological perspective there can be no freedom in the long run without recognition of interdependence. One man's freedom to burn his trash will violate everyone's freedom to breathe healthy air. We no longer live on the frontier from which we could move on if we felt crowded or found the resources depleted. When the community faces common dangers, government inaction may be a greater threat than intelligent regulatory action. In the past we have usually thought of virtue in individual terms; today the ethics of social decisions are crucial. Individualistic values must give place to social values in a world where we breathe or suffocate together. The real threat to our freedom occurs when we have lost control of technology; we are frustrated by our impotence in dealing with an impersonal process which seems to have taken over, a set of forces which control us.

The balance between *freedom* and *control* has already been mentioned at a number of points (genetic control, population control, pollution control). Total freedom in any of these areas will lead to the violation of human dignity, since the freedom of one man or one corporation can harm so many people. But human dignity is violated also when too much control is introduced and persons are manipulated like objects. There is no general formula for balancing the opposing risks of individualism and collectivism. One can only try to evaluate the extent of public danger from uncontrolled actions in each specific area, and then legislate the minimum controls necessary to further the welfare of society. One can try to keep the instruments of control within democratic political processes so that government agencies are responsible to the electorate. Technology does provide new temptations for the abuse of political power, yet the redirection of technology can only be accomplished by the responsible use of such power.

Daniel Bell has argued that despite the emergence of a technical elite, *the politician rather than the technician* will dominate in future decisions. He believes that flexibility, diversity, and responsibility to the electorate are still possible within the planning process. Political issues, far from vanishing, will be more overt as the consequences of alternative actions are more apparent. Value choices, such as allocation of the costs of environmental deterioration, will be more explicit. He foresees greater popular involvement in political debate when greater leisure is prevalent; there will also be a wider scope for congressional legislation.[23] Society, in other words, will be able to apply suitable feedbacks to control the controllers. There is already a new awareness that ecological decisions affecting all of us should be matters of public policy decided through political processes; this attitude must be extended to other types of legislation concerning technology. We also need better channels for members of Congress to receive scientific advice. There are virtually no experts in science among senators or their aides. (Thus until quite late in the debate on antiballistic missiles (ABM), senators were almost entirely dependent on the judgment of Defense Department spokesmen.)

To coordinate long-range planning a *Department of Science and Technology* is needed. Donald Hornig, President Johnson's science adviser, has advocated such a department with a cabinet-level secretary.[24] It is ridiculous that the Post Office should be represented on the Cabinet, while science is not. The department should have sufficient authority and funds to set basic science policy and to coordinate scientific programs throughout government agencies. It would include both natural and social scientists trained to study and evaluate the social effects of alternative technological developments, in order both to guide policy decisions and to suggest legislation for the regulatory powers which would be required to prevent harmful effects. The department would also promote research in federal laboratories, universities, and interdisciplinary institutes on scientific problems of particular social significance, including international disarmament and peace-keeping mechanisms.

A separate *Department of Environment and Population* is probably also desirable. It would sponsor research and promote regulatory legislation on pollution-reducing methods, population control, environmental preservation, and consumer protection. Ideally these activities could occur within a single ecologically-conscious department of science, technology, and environment —which would avoid proliferating agencies, especially ones which might work at cross-purposes. But the problems of combining these functions is evident in the history of the Atomic Energy Commission, which was entrusted with both the development of nuclear energy and the provision of regulations to protect citizens and environments; the AEC has frequently underestimated the radiation dangers from the projects in which it was engaged, and has seldom studied with adequate care the consequences of its decisions. It would therefore seem preferable that two separate departments, each provided with substantial funds and authority and working closely with well-informed congressional committees, should develop and administer the redirection of technology in this crucial stage of human history.

IV. Conclusions: On National Priorities

I will close, then, by summarizing the most urgent issues of science policy today. Some of the problems discussed in this volume raise interesting ethical questions in the more distant future (genetic control, leisure, and perhaps androids someday); others represent impending crises which demand our immediate attention. We must be open to a radically new future, but we must remember that the future always grows out of the present—whose problems the utopian prophets of a new era usually neglect. In order of importance I would list four problems which should be at the top of our agenda; if we fail to solve them the future of man will be dark indeed:[25]

1. Nuclear War. We have lived with the threat of nuclear holocaust for so many years that we have forgotten its capacity to destroy the fabric of civilized life, if not the habitability of the planet itself. President Kennedy is said to have estimated that the chance of nuclear war at the time of the Cuba crisis was 25 per cent; because we have gambled already without losing, we assume we can safely continue to gamble. Meanwhile, we put into military budgets hundreds of billions which are desperately needed elsewhere. Though nuclear disarmament is largely a political question, it has many scientific aspects. If we were seriously concerned, we would not only take stronger diplomatic initiatives but would devote substantial sums to research on detection devices and ways of enforcing disarmament agreements. Instead, we start a new round of nuclear escalation by constructing an **ABM** system whose effectiveness is highly debatable. When will we have the courage and wisdom to accept the necessity of a world order, and to develop the institutions it will require: a genuine world government, international courts with compulsory jurisdiction, and an international police force?

2. Population control. Famine, poverty, and social chaos resulting from overpopulation in underdeveloped countries are imminent threats of disaster. I indicated that population pressure is also a serious challenge to technologically advanced countries, since it greatly aggravates pollution, urban blight, racial tension, and other social problems—yet it has received little attention in recent national policy discussions. Birth control alone is of limited value, because the wanted child crowds the earth just as much as the unwanted child. I maintained, however, that drastic compulsory measures should not be attempted so long as considerable promise is held out by intensive voluntary methods: education for smaller families, social and economic incentives and pressures, research on long-lasting chemical contraception, etc.

3. Poverty and hunger. Technology, I suggested, is increasing the gap between the affluent and the poor, and must be deliberately redirected to reduce this gap. On a global scale this re-quires a greatly expanded, internationally controlled program of technical assistance to underdeveloped countries for agricul-tural and industrial modernization. On the national scale it demands intensive efforts for the rehabilitation of the urban ghetto. I have urged that human misery on our own earth should have higher priority than landing a man on Mars. But only the reduction of defense expenditures around the world will release funds of the magnitude needed, and only an effec-tive world government can deal with problems which are global in character. Conversely, overpopulation, hunger, and poverty add to the danger of nuclear war. The items on our agenda are clearly interlocking.

4. Environmental deterioration. I suggested earlier that the ecological crisis reflects our exploitative attitudes toward na-ture as well as toward our fellow man. Fetid rivers, polluted lakes, and acrid air testify to our failure to recognize our inter-dependence with the natural order and with each other. We have allowed technology to be an instrument of private profit and assumed that it would lead to human welfare. But now it must be subjected to greater public control through political processes if its potential contribution to man's life is to be realized. If the misuse of technology has been the cause of many of our most pressing problems, only its redirection can enable us to avoid calamity. The global interdependence of this space-ship earth, on which we travel together to a common destiny, demands once more an international approach to world re-sources. It is now within man's power to achieve a world from which are banished man's ancient enemies: war, disease, hun-ger, and poverty.

I have urged, finally, that man's unprecedented power over his future calls for responsible maturity and openness to crea-tive possibilities. A *Christian secularity* must be deeply concerned about life in this world. The gospel is not the enemy of human freedom and fulfillment, but liberates us to discover our au-thentic humanity. To the redirection of technology the biblical message can bring a passion for social justice and a prophetic concern for a more humane social order. It provides a perspective for the evaluation of culture, a basis for critical reflection on the ends of human existence, and a motive for the defense of human dignity. It can encourage sensitivity to the effects of technology on people and the dangers when productive efficiency becomes our main goal. It stands in judgment on a society of consumers in frantic pursuit of material comfort, a culture which inculcates competitive rather than cooperative attitudes. For man's choice of life styles and his decisions about the uses of technology reflect his most basic values and ideals.

The distinctive task of the servant church is *to safeguard the human.* The biblical message holds up both an ideal of social justice and a model of man as a responsible self. The church must not only help to redirect technology but must keep us aware of dimensions of life inaccessible to technical reason. It can be an agent for the cultivation of feeling, the enrichment and intensification of experience, the development of modes of thought not reducible to computer programs. In a technological age, men and women need an awareness of their own capacities, and of the range of ways of being human. The church should encourage the artist and the poet as well as the social reformer. It should present leisure as an opportunity for service, self-discovery, and celebration. Here, once more, the biblical concern for personal and interpersonal existence is an important corrective to the depersonalizing tendencies of a technological society.

But our concern must always be directed to *man in nature,* not man over against nature. In reacting to the ecological crisis it is not enough simply to attack one symptom after another, or to look to the government for solutions. As long as man's attitude toward nature is basically exploitative, he will find new ways to violate the web of life. Although the doctrine of man's dominion over nature is one of the roots of the crisis, there are other biblical themes which could correct against it. I have stressed the interdependence of all creatures, the unity of man with the natural order, and the need for a more clearly articulated theology of nature. A sense of the sanctity and harmony of all life would make us more aware of the impact of technology on nature.

What is needed, then, is a reorientation of values and goals, a shift from a *"thing-oriented"* to a *"person-oriented"* and *"life-oriented"* culture. Such a society would be dedicated to the development of human resources within the community of life of which man is a part. This will require an imaginative vision of the future, a sense of responsibility to children yet unborn— including affirmation of their right to inherit a habitable environment. Our new context is global interdependence. In a day of television intercommunication and economic interaction, events impinge on us from around the world. The extreme inequalities in the distribution of technology-based affluence cannot be allowed to continue.

I do not mean to neglect the importance of *individual action.* There is a lot you can do as an individual. You can use biodegradable detergents and returnable bottles, and you can take public transportation whenever possible. You can resolve to adopt, if you want more than two children in your family, and encourage others to do the same. You can cut down on excessive consumption, and put pressure on industry to orient production toward fundamental rather than marginal needs. You can support uses of leisure which are active and creative rather than the passive entertainment of spectators. You can promote small discussion groups in the context of work, neighborhood, church or community.[26] There is no substitute for personal responsibility in your own actions. But above all you can participate in democratic political processes. For I have argued that in a technological society the crucial questions involve national policy, not only in the public sector (education, health, transportation, housing, recreation) but in the guidance of applied science.

Technology must be redirected *to reduce the gap between the rich and the poor,* the inequalities between the "haves" and the "have-nots," both at home and abroad. We must use technology to abolish poverty and hunger, not to produce more luxury goods. At the moment billions are spent on advertising to stimulate new desires, while for many people basic needs go unmet. Space and military technology is highly developed, but little deliberate effort has been given to the technology of urban housing. We have the technical ability and the organizational skills to fulfill man's dream of peace and plenty, once we take seriously our professed ideals of justice and equality.

The redirection of technology, in sum, is the crucial challenge of this decade. Man can still decide his future before it is too late. He can act to fulfill the promise: "Earth shall be fair, and all her people one." Technology can yet be man's servant rather than his master. In the words of Deuteronomy: *"I have set before you life and death . . . ; therefore choose life"* (30:19).

Notes

ONE The Scientific Method

1. From Anthony Towne, "God is Dead in Georgia," *Motive*, February, 1966. Used by permission of *Motive* magazine.
2. See Ian G. Barbour, *Issues in Science and Religion* (Englewood Cliffs, N. J.: Prentice-Hall, Inc., 1966), Chap. 8.
3. See Mary B. Hesse, "Models and Analogy in Science," in P. Edwards, ed., *Encyclopedia of Philosophy* (New York: The Macmillan Co., 1967), Vol. 5.
4. Hans Freudenthal, ed., *The Concept and the Role of the Model in Mathematics and Natural and Social Sciences* (New York: Gordon and Breach, 1961).
5. Mary B. Hesse, *Models and Analogies in Science* (London: Sheed and Ward, 1963).
6. Jacques Hadamard, *Essay on the Psychology of Invention in the Mathematical Field* (Princeton, N. J.: Princeton University Press, 1964).
7. William Thomson (Lord Kelvin), *Baltimore Lectures* (Baltimore: Johns Hopkins University, 1904), p. 187.
8. Richard Braithwaite, *Scientific Explanation* (Cambridge: Cambridge University Press, 1953), Chap. 5; compare Ernest Nagel, *The Structure of Science* (New York: Harcourt, Brace & World, 1961), pp. 107–117.
9. See, for example, Philipp Frank, *Philosophy of Science* (Englewood Cliffs, N. J.: Prentice-Hall, Inc., 1957), Chap. 9.

10. Neils Bohr, *Atomic Physics and Human Knowledge* (New York: John Wiley & Sons, 1958), pp. 39 ff.
11. Leonard Nash, *The Nature of Natural Science* (Boston: Little, Brown & Co., 1963), p. 251.
12. H. Richard Niebuhr, *The Meaning of Revelation* (New York: The Macmillan Co., 1941), Chap. 3.
13. Edwyn Bevan, *Symbolism and Belief* (London: George Allen & Unwin, 1938).
14. See H. D. Lewis, *Our Experience of God* (London: George Allen & Unwin, 1959).
15. William Austin, "Waves, Particles and Paradoxes," *Rice University Studies,* Vol. 53 (1967), pp. 93 ff.
16. Richard Braithwaite, *An Empiricist's View of the Nature of Religious Belief* (Cambridge: Cambridge University Press, 1955).
17. See Donald Evans, *The Logic of Self-Involvement* (London: SCM Press, 1963); Ian Ramsey, *Religious Language* (London: SCM Press, 1957), Chap. 2; also Ian Ramsey, *Models and Mystery* (London: Oxford University Press, 1964).
18. N. R. Hanson, *Patterns of Discovery* (Cambridge: Cambridge University Press, 1958), Chap. 1; cf. Michael Polanyi, *Personal Knowledge* (Chicago: University of Chicago Press, 1958).
19. See Israel Scheffler, *Science and Subjectivity* (Indianapolis: The Bobbs-Merrill Co., 1967); also Mary Hesse, "Theory and Observation: Is There an Independent Observation Language?," to appear in Vol. IV of the Pittsburgh Philosophy of Science series (1970).
20. P. K. Feyerabend, "Explanation, Reduction and Empiricism," in Herbert Feigl and Grover Maxwell, eds., *Minnesota Studies in the Philosophy of Science* (Minneapolis: University of Minnesota Press, 1962), Vol. III.
21. Cited in R. G. Swinburne, "The Falsifiability of Scientific Theories," *Mind,* July, 1964, p. 434.
22. Thomas S. Kuhn, *The Structure of Scientific Revolutions* (Chicago: University of Chicago Press, 1962), pp. 147, 149.
23. Ninian Smart, *Reasons and Faiths* (London: Routledge & Kegan Paul, 1958).
24. See Ronald Hepburn, *Christianity and Paradox* (London: C. A. Watts & Co., 1958), Chap. 11.
25. Frederick Ferré, "Metaphors, Models and Religion," *Soundings,* Vol. 51 (1968), 341; see also his "Mapping the Logic of Models in Science and Theology," *The Christian Scholar,* Vol. 46 (1963), 31.
26. John Hick, *Faith and Knowledge,* 2nd ed. (London: Macmillan & Co., 1967), Chap. 6.
27. Niebuhr, *The Meaning of Revelation,* Chap. 1; Paul Tillich, *Dynamics of Faith* (New York: Harper & Row, 1957), Chap. 1.

TWO   The Autonomy of Nature

1. Karl Barth, *Church Dogmatics* (Edinburgh: T. & T. Clark, 1958), Vol. 3, Part 3, p. 148.
2. See, for example, Reginald Garrigou-Lagrange, *God: His Existence and His Nature* (St. Louis: Herder, 1934); or Benignus Gerrity, *Nature, Knowledge and God* (Milwaukee: Bruce, 1947).
3. Thomas J. J. Altizer, *The Gospel of Christian Atheism* (Philadelphia: Westminster Press, 1966).
4. Langdon Gilkey, "Cosmology, Ontology, and the Travail of Biblical Language," *Journal of Religion*, Vol. 41 (1961), 200.
5. Martin Buber, *I and Thou*, trans. R. G. Smith (Edinburgh: T. & T. Clark, 1937).
6. Rudolf Bultmann, *Kerygma and Myth*, ed. H. Bartsch (London: S. P. C. K., 1953; New York: Harper Torchbooks).
7. Rudolf Bultmann, *Jesus Christ and Mythology* (New York: Charles Scribner's Sons, 1958), pp. 62, 65.
8. See Donald D. Evans, *The Logic of Self-Involvement* (London: SCM Press, 1963); Frederick Ferré, *Basic Modern Philosophy of Religion* (New York: Charles Scribner's Sons, 1967), Chap. 13.
9. See T. R. Miles, *Religion and the Scientific Outlook* (London: George Allen & Unwin, 1959), Chaps. 8–10.
10. Alan R. White, ed., *The Philosophy of Action* (London: Oxford University Press, 1968).
11. Gordon Kaufman, "On the Meaning of 'Act of God,'" *Harvard Theological Review*, Vol. 61 (1968), 175.
12. Alfred North Whitehead, *Science and the Modern World* (New York: The Macmillan Co., 1925); see also Ivor Leclerc, *Whitehead's Metaphysics* (New York: The Macmillan Co., 1958); Charles Hartshorne, *Reality as Social Process* (Glencoe, Ill.: The Free Press, 1953); John B. Cobb, *A Christian Natural Theology* (Philadelphia: Westminster Press, 1965).
13. Alfred North Whitehead, *Process and Reality* (New York: The Macmillan Co., 1929), p. 532.
14. Dietrich Bonhoeffer, *Letters and Papers from Prison* (New York: The Macmillan Co., 1962), p. 219.
15. Werner Heisenberg, *Physics and Philosophy* (New York: Harper & Row, 1958), p. 181.
16. Theodosius Dobzhansky, "Scientific Explanation: Chance and Antichance in Organic Evolution," in B. Baumrin, ed., *Philosophy of Science* (New York: Interscience, 1963), Vol. 1.
17. George Gaylord Simpson, *This View of Life* (New York: Harcourt, Brace & World, 1964), Chaps. 7, 9; Ernst Mayr, "Cause and Effect in Biology," *Science*, Vol. 134 (1961), 1501.
18. Alister Hardy, *The Living Stream* (London: Collins, 1965), Chap. 6;

see also Charles Birch, *Nature and God* (London: SCM Press, 1965).
19. Pierre Teilhard de Chardin, *The Phenomenon of Man*, trans. B. Wall (New York: Harper & Row, 1959).
20. See Ian G. Barbour, "Five Ways of Reading Teilhard," *Soundings*, Vol. 51 (1968), 155; also "Teilhard's Process Metaphysics," *Journal of Religion*, Vol. 49 (1969), 136.
21. John B. Cobb, *God and the World* (Philadelphia: Westminster Press, 1969); Eugene Peters, *The Creative Advance* (St. Louis: Bethany Press, 1966); Peter Hamilton, *The Living God and the Modern World* (Philadelphia: Pilgrim Press, 1967); Norman Pittenger, *Alfred North Whitehead* (Richmond, Va.: John Knox Press, 1969).

THREE   The Technological Mentality

1. Arend van Leeuwen, *Christianity in World History*, tr. H. H. Hoskins (New York: Charles Scribner's Sons, 1965).
2. Friedrich Gogarten, *The Reality of Faith*, tr. C. Michalson (Philadelphia: Westminster Press, 1959); see also Ronald Gregor Smith, *Secular Christianity* (New York: Harper & Row, 1966); Larry Shiner, *The Secularization of History* (Nashville: Abingdon Press, 1966).
3. Dietrich Bonhoeffer, *Letters and Papers from Prison*, tr. R. Fuller (New York: The Macmillan Co., 1953); see also Harry E. Smith, *Secularization and the University* (Richmond, Va.: John Knox Press, 1968).
4. Robert Theobald, "New Possibilities of Modern Technology," in Denys Munby, ed., *Economic Growth in World Perspective* (New York: Association Press, 1966).
5. Harvey Cox, *The Secular City* (New York: The Macmillan Co., 1965); Myron B. Bloy, *The Crisis of Cultural Change* (New York: The Seabury Press, 1965); Emmanuel G. Mesthene, "What Modern Science Offers the Church," *Saturday Review*, November 19, 1966, p. 29.
6. Jacques Ellul, *The Technological Society*, tr. J. Wilkinson (New York: Alfred A. Knopf, 1964).
7. See annual reports of Harvard University Program on Technology and Society.
8. Lynn White, Jr., "The Historical Roots of Our Ecological Crisis," *Science*, Vol. 155 (1967), 1203.
9. C.F.D. Moule, *Man and Nature in the New Testament* (Philadelphia: Fortress Press, 1967).
10. Frederick Elder, *Crisis in Eden* (Nashville: Abingdon Press, 1970); see also Richard A. Baer, "Conservation: An Arena for the Church's Action," *Christian Century*, Jan. 8, 1969, p. 40.
11. Herbert Marcuse, *One-Dimensional Man* (Boston: Beacon Press, 1964); Theodore Roszak, *The Making of a Counter Culture* (Garden City, N.Y.: Doubleday & Co., 1969).

12. See Roger L. Shinn, *Man: The New Humanism* (Philadelphia: Westminster Press, 1968).
13. See Cameron P. Hall, *Technology and People* (Valley Forge, Pa.: Judson Press, 1969).
14. Wayne H. Davis, "Overpopulated America," *The New Republic*, Jan. 10, 1970, p. 14.
15. Huston Smith, "Technology and Human Values: This American Moment," in Cameron Hall, ed., *Human Values and Advancing Technology* (New York: Friendship Press, 1967), p. 28.

FOUR Biochemical Man

1. Francis Crick, *Of Molecules and Men* (Seattle: University of Washington Press, 1966), pp. 14, 98.
2. See Carl Hempel, *Philosophy of Natural Science* (Englewood Cliffs, N. J.: Prentice-Hall, Inc., 1966), Chap. 7; Ernest Nagel, *The Structure of Science* (New York: Harcourt, Brace & World, 1961), Chaps. 11, 12.
3. C. Grobstein, "Levels and Ontogeny," *American Scientist*, Vol. 50 (1962), 52; Ludwig Von Bertalanffy, *Problems of Life* (London: C. A. Watts and Co., 1952), Chap. 5.
4. G. G. Simpson, *This View of Life* (New York: Harcourt, Brace & World, 1964), Chap. 6; Bentley Glass, "The Relation of the Physical Sciences to Biology," in B. Baumrin, ed., *Philosophy of Science* (New York: Interscience Publishers, 1963), Vol. 1, p. 243.
5. Morton Beckner, *The Biological Way of Thought* (New York: Columbia University Press, 1959).
6. Emerson Shideler, "Darwin and the Doctrine of Man," *Journal of Religion*, July 1960, p. 198; W. H. Thorpe, *Science, Man and Morals* (London: Methuen & Co., 1965).
7. Theodosius Dobzhansky, *The Biology of Ultimate Concern* (New York: New American Library, 1967).
8. José Delgado, "Brain Technology and Psychocivilization" in C. P. Hall, ed., *Human Values and Advancing Technology* (New York: Friendship Press, 1967).
9. H. W. Robinson, *Religious Ideas of the Old Testament* (London: Gerald Duckworth & Co., 1913), p. 83; Oscar Cullmann, *Immortality of the Soul or Resurrection of the Dead?* (New York: The Macmillan Co., 1958), p. 30.
10. Leroy Augenstein, *Come, Let Us Play God* (New York: Harper & Row, 1969).
11. Hermann J. Muller, "Means and Aims in Human Genetic Betterment," in T. M. Sonneborn, ed., *The Control of Human Heredity and Evolution* (New York: The Macmillan Co., 1965).
12. See Albert Rosenfeld, *Second Genesis: The Coming Control of Life* (En-

glewood Cliffs, N. J.: Prentice-Hall, Inc., 1969), Chap. 2.

13. Jean Rostand, *Can Man be Modified?* (New York: Basic Books, 1959).

14. David Townsend, "Common-Sense Looks at Man-Made Man," *Religion in Life,* Summer, 1961, p. 443.

15. Paul Ramsey, "Moral and Religious Implications of Genetic Control," in J. D. Roslansky, ed., *Genetics and the Future of Man* (Amsterdam: North Holland Publishing Co., 1966).

16. See Gerald Kelly, *Medico-Moral Problems* (St. Louis: The Catholic Hospital Press, 1958), p. 228.

17. F. A. Simmons, *Fertility and Sterility,* Vol. 8 (1957), 547; J. A. Haman, *California Medical Journal,* Vol. 90 (1959), 130.

18. E. Farris and M. Garrison, *Obstetrics and Gynecology,* Vol. 3 (1954), 19.

19. G. Gerstel, *American Journal of Psychiatry,* Vol. 17 (1963), 64.

20. John Gordon, "Some Legal Considerations," in "New Considerations of Artificial Insemination Donor," an excellent report prepared by the Science and Society Program, North Carolina State University, Raleigh, N. C. (1969); the latter includes Karl Ostrom, "Psychological Aspects," from which references 17-19 above are taken.

21. Theodosius Dobzhansky, *Heredity and the Nature of Man* (New York: Harcourt, Brace & World, 1964), Chap. 5; cf. John M. Smith, "Eugenics and Utopia," *Daedalus,* Spring, 1965, p. 487.

22. Roger L. Shinn, "Genetic Decisions: A Case Study in Ethical Method," in *Soundings,* Vol. 52 (1969), 299.

23. Quoted in Rosenfeld, *op. cit.,* pp. 91-92.

24. Quoted in Fleming, "On Living in a Biological Revolution," *Atlantic,* February, 1969, p. 67.

25. Augenstein, *op. cit.,* Chap. 7.

26. Delgado, *op. cit.,* p. 81.

FIVE   The Cybernetic Revolution

1. Hubert L. Dreyfus, *Alchemy and Artificial Intelligence* (Santa Monica, Cal.: Rand Corporation, 1965); Edward Feigenbaum and Julian Feldman, eds., *Computers and Thought* (New York: McGraw-Hill, 1963).

2. See Huston Smith, "Human versus Artificial Intelligence," in J. D. Roslansky, ed., *The Human Mind* (Amsterdam: North-Holland Publishing Co., 1968).

3. Kenneth Sayre, "Human and Mechanical Recognition," in K. M. Sayre and F. J. Crosson, eds., *The Modeling of Mind* (Notre Dame, Ind.: Univ. of Notre Dame Press, 1963).

4. Marvin Minsky, "Artificial Intelligence," *Scientific American,* Sept. 1966.

5. Frederick Crosson and Kenneth Sayre, "Modeling: Simulation and Replication," in Sayre and Crosson, *op. cit.*

6. Donald G. Fink, *Computers and the Human Mind* (Garden City, N. Y.: Doubleday & Co., 1966), Chap. 10.

7. Ulric Neisser, "The Imitation of Man by Machine," *Science,* Vol. 139 (1963), 197: Hubert Dreyfus, "Why Computers Must Have Bodies in Order to be Intelligent," *Review of Metaphysics,* Vol. 21 (1967), 13.

8. See Alan R. Anderson, ed., *Minds and Machines* (Englewood Cliffs, N. J.: Prentice-Hall, Inc., 1964); Kenneth Sayre, *Consciousness: A Philosophic Study of Minds and Machines* (New York: Random House, 1969).

9. See reference 4 above; also the Introduction in Marvin Minsky, ed., *Semantic Information Processing* (Cambridge: The MIT Press, 1968).

10. Donald Michael, "Cybernation: The Silent Conquest," in M. Philipson, ed., *Automation: Implications for the Future* (New York: Vintage Books, 1962); John G. Burke, ed., *The New Technology and Human Values* (Belmont, Cal.: Wadsworth Publishing Co., 1966), Part II.

11. Robert Theobald, "Cybernetics and the Problems of Social Reorganization," in Charles Dechert, ed., *The Social Impact of Cybernetics* (Notre Dame, Ind.: Univ. of Notre Dame Press, 1966); also his "New Possibilities of Modern Technology," in Denys Munby, ed., *Economic Growth in World Perspective* (New York: Association Press, 1966).

12. Robert Lee, *Religion and Leisure in America* (Nashville: Abingdon Press, 1964).

13. Josef Pieper, *Leisure: The Basis of Culture* (New York: Pantheon Books, 1952); Sebastian de Grazia, *Of Time, Work and Leisure* (New York: Doubleday & Co., 1964).

14. Charles K. Brightbill, *The Challenge of Leisure* (Englewood Cliffs, N. J.: Prentice-Hall, 1960).

15. William Brickman and Stanley Lehrer, eds., *Automation, Education and Human Values* (New York: School & Society Books, 1966).

16. Murray Modal, "Voting Simulation: The Manufacture of Consent," in Philipson, *op. cit.;* Joe McGinnis, *The Selling of the President, 1968* (New York: Trident Press, 1969).

17. Arthur R. Miller, "The National Data Center and the Invasion of Privacy," *Atlantic,* November, 1967; "The Computer and the Invasion of Privacy," House Committee on Government Operations (1966), Cornelius Gallagher, chairman.

18. See R. MacBride, *The Automated State* (Philadelphia: Chilton Book Co., 1967).

19. Norman Faramelli, "Systems Analysis and Social Problem Solving," *Soundings,* Vol. 52 (1969), 272.

20. Robert Boguslaw, *The New Utopians: A Study of System Design and Social*

Change (Englewood Cliffs, N. J.: Prentice-Hall, Inc., 1965), Chap. 8.

21. Gordon Davies, "Describing Men to Machines: The Use of Computers in Dealing with Social Problems," *Soundings,* Vol. 52 (1969), 283.

22. John McDermott, "Technology: The Opiate of the Intellectuals," *New York Review of Books,* July 31, 1969, p. 25.

SIX The Redirection of Technology

1. John Platt, "What We Must Do," *Science,* Vol. 166 (1969), 1121.
2. An earlier version of this case study appeared as "On to Mars?" in *Christian Century,* November 19, 1969, p. 1478. Copyright 1969, Christian Century Foundation; used by permission.
3. Vernon Van Dyke, *Pride and Power: The Rationale of the Space Program* (Urbana: University of Illinois Press, 1964). Also critical is Amitai Etzioni, *The Moon-Doggle* (Garden City, N. Y.: Doubleday & Co., 1964). For a defense of the space program, see Neil P. Ruzig, *The Case for Going to the Moon* (New York: G. P. Putnam's Sons, 1965); Edward B. Lindaman, *Space: A New Direction for Mankind* (New York: Harper & Row, 1969).
4. Ralph E. Lapp, *The New Priesthood* (New York: Harper & Row, 1965), Chap. 8.
5. Philip Abelson (before Committee on Aeronautical and Space Sciences, U. S. Senate, 1965) in John G. Burke, ed., *The New Technology and Human Values* (Belmont, Cal.: Wadsworth Publishing Co., 1966), p. 356.
6. Alvin Weinberg, *Reflections on Big Science* (Cambridge: M. I. T. Press, 1967), pp. 65-84.
7. *New York Times,* September 18, 1969, p. 1; *Newsweek,* September 29, 1969.
8. "Earth Resources Satellite System," House Committee on Science and Astronautics, 1969.
9. The September, 1969, issue of *Bulletin of the Atomic Scientists* is devoted to "Man on the Moon."
10. Figures from World Population Data Sheet (1968), Population Reference Bureau, Washington D. C.; Paul H. Ehrlich, *The Population Bomb* (New York: Ballantine Books, 1968).
11. Roger Revelle, "Can Man Domesticate Himself?", *Bulletin of the Atomic Scientists,* Vol. 22 (1966), 2; Larry Ng and Stuart Mudd, eds., *The Population Crisis* (Bloomington: Indiana University Press, 1965).
12. Lincoln and Alice Day, *Too Many Americans* (New York: Dell Publishing Co., 1965); Garrett Hardin, ed., *Population, Evolution, and Birth Control,* 2nd ed. (San Francisco: W. H. Freeman Co., 1969).